"A sensitive character study, a wise a chronicle of place: Goodman accomplishes so much. Jack Houghteling's voice is both rich and economical, original and familiar with the deepest registers of observation and reflection, illuminating a range of experience, from the technological to the deeply human."

—Daniel Mason,
Author of *The Piano Tuner* and *A Registry of My Passage Upon the Earth*, a Pulitzer Prize finalist

"If you prefer novels that slot tidily into familiar genre pigeonholes, look elsewhere. Jack Houghteling's Goodman is a wholly sui generis creation: at once dignified epistle and crackling polemic, quiet domestic drama and comedy of digital manners, Kerouackish ramble across America and Rothian character study. Really, though, you come for the prose, a torrent of neologisms, digressions, nested clauses, bizarrely apt descriptions, and pop-cultural ephemera that overflows this book's banks like a stream in floodstage. Goodman is the linguistically subversive work of a writer who obviously adores the English language, but isn't afraid to give it the occasional wet willy."

—Ben Goldfarb,
Author of *Eager,* winner of the 2019 PEN/E.O. Wilson Literary Science Writing Award

"Goodman is a strange, beautiful, original and inventive journey. Jack Houghteling arranges his sentences like a mad composer. There's true literary power here. I am grateful; I have found a new writer to admire."

—Gabriel Bump,
Author of *Everywhere You Don't Belong*

"Showing the real and telling its feel – this is the task and Jack Houghteling does not shirk from it."

—Joshua Cohen,
Author of *The Netanyahus* and *Book of Numbers*

"Written in a daring high-style, Goodman is a novel I won't soon forget by an author to watch."

—Elliot Ackerman,
Author of *Dark at the Crossing*, a
National Book Award finalist

"In this sensitive portrait of a May-December friendship, Jack Houghteling casts a scrutinizing yet affectionate gaze at his generation's attempts to navigate this bizarre historical epoch. With beauty and wit, Goodman explores the question of how to live an authentic life in the age of technological inauthenticity."

—Kate Greathead, Author
of *Laura and Emma*

GOODMAN

GOODMAN

A novel

by

JACK HOUGHTELING

Adelaide Books
New York / Lisbon
2022

GOODMAN
A novel
By Jack Houghteling

Copyright © by Jack Houghteling

Cover design © 2022 by Jack Houghteling & George duPont

Published by Adelaide Books, New York / Lisbon
adelaidebooks.org
Editor-in-Chief
Stevan V. Nikolic

For any information, please address Adelaide Books
at info@adelaidebooks.org
or write to:
Adelaide Books
244 Fifth Ave. Suite D27
New York, NY, 10001

ISBN-10: 978-1-956635-86-7

Printed in the United States of America

To Dad and Fiora.

Foreword

There is a quandary to a name like Goodman, which has been the working title of this expanding, contracting, re-forming work since its original 130,000 word draft (over four times the size of its current length). It satisfies the titular imperative – an acceptance that all creative wholes have names, some of which mean everything and others positively less than everything.

It can be taken simply – this is a story about a man, and he is good.

Yet it also broaches an irreconcilability, many irreconcilabilities: of a privileged son seeking to take part in a world of pain, injustice and tension to which he wasn't born, even as he acknowledges that fact, renounces it, questions how one can even make such a renunciation to begin with; of a man, a brain about him and a body beneath him, seeking to feed on the infinite spiritual calories of the universe in a life in which he is not infinite.

The first impasse we have collectively taken increasing interest in as a society that is built on inherited power and unjust gain, and we've done so in many forms – on the street corners of summer, through ballot submittal, through the Serif and Helvetica of the web.

The second impasse finds home within the penumbra of humanism - its demands, its wonderances - and the seriousness and uncertainty of, in GOODMAN's case, the American Romantic and Odyssean traditions that shepherd it (and which, of course, far outshine it), from Melville and Dickinson to Terry Southern and Nathanael West.

Tim Goodman learns in the nascent years of his life to sacrifice ease for decency. The narrator, a Les Incompetents carrying couches out of cellar doors, seeks that truth in the substance of his own flowing, spilling brain – in the device that cups his hand, thumb to pinky. What does it mean, then and there, or here and now, to be good? Perhaps the answer can only be found on a car ride; in a car crash; on the tail of a fast-moving gale.

I sit here in a small square room in a building full of small square rooms. I fiddle with my silver computer head. I scroll through my phone, flicking my left thumb across the screen, bottom to top. Pics, geotags, humble meditation, humor, pall, wit, aphorism and substance all flow by me. The many classes of self-advertisement. The desirous will to connect. I wonder how I got back here again.

Sometimes they don't flow, but edge – buffering speed – in light of an error in satellite transmission. A fault of air.

The cold light outside my window weakens and fades across Great Dover Street, removed, distant, southeastward. It finally begins to drop at about half past four. At five, the sun's bottom half touches Brixton. At five-thirty, it is gone, the southern sky vestiges of gas and fire, the northern sky veiled, planetary, indigo.

I exit my excursion, continuing to wonder how I got back here, how I had of no way of knowing how I got back here, the *here's* will to stay based on its will to exist, extend, diffuse – textual, vocal, visual; career, education, friendship, relationship, family; love, fear, hope.

Once I'm offline, I sit, not yet standing. I breathe heavily.

Then, again, I am wayward: phone to computer, music to writing, writing to reading, reading to phone, upright to chair back to upright. I continue to think. I think hard – if not well – struggling to summon a subject to view. When I do, the impressions are half-empty, depthless. They lose steam, are obstructed by photos from Mexico City, by political supposition in the form of post. They dim out like bad movies.

I conceptualize the shored up sentence. What will it look like? Then I move away from sentences. Elements. Surface area. I start with the regionally specific: meaty, colorful face. Sympathetic eyes. Sharp, searchful brows in want of impetus, something to think about, to be just-enough dissatisfied with. High, loose voice. Funny, but solemnly wary of fluff, of the deleterious. Bad breather. Thick, soft body.

Then, the spirit: total and nearing enough of a form to spark my inaugural efforts to come to the page, ghostly and brief enough to inspire my will to elucidate.

I release myself to my feet. I unveil my headphones. My ears feel the indentations of the buds at their point of prior residence. I walk past the bathroom – built into the cubic penumbra of my small living unit – and out into the hallway, not yet sure where I'm going, walking, Tubing. While stalled at the elevator, I pull out my phone to a blank buffer. I recall why: the hallway has no Wi-Fi.

I sit back down in my chair. This time the weight of my digressions feels lighter, my head's din replaced with cool blue evening light, birdsong (the ones that get played in the last weeks of winter, that live atop the Gulf Stream's crest), the footballers of Tabard Gardens, chanting back and forth to one another in Midlands and Yorkshire and West African-tinged estuary, streaking down the sides of the field, carioca-ing, kicking.

I begin again as I intended, seeking out the note. At first all I see is him in the driver's seat. We're driving down Route 20 to Pittsfield. One of those relieving summer days, wet, slightly humid. Both of us are a Celsius degree away from sweating. The car is safely going fifteen miles over the speed limit, a thirty that should be forty (maladministration on the part of Boston), though he does appear to be trying to get somewhere. To one of those atypical small business closing times - 3:45, 4:20.

The rain, intermittent, heavies the large-bodied leaves of the sugar maples, which, when they drop, flip and funnel in unison - by the motile force of their wide torsos - rather than wave and flutter.

In another alteration he's sitting on the bank of his pond, shirt off, the bank formed by a ring of levee-sized fieldstones. My parents said he used to be much bigger, that marriage of sturdy muscular build and poor eating habits, but here and now he can't be much more than 190. He is all bone and loose flesh; flesh which hangs toward his right because his right leg, hindered and complicated by a knee made of strong bone and tendon but festering cartilage, is pondward. His left side keeps his body elevated, rock-side. His ankles are swollen. His face is perfectly shaven. He looks west, out toward the tree line, toward the border of New York and Massachusetts just hundreds of yards away.

I try starting from elsewhere. I think about alternate locations, all razored down monosyllables of grander, unelaborated possibilities. Then, images.

Hot train platform.

Waterfront sprawl, the sprawl of prior industry.

The river, toxified by the sprawl as it continued on in ambidextrous north-south intermittency (*Muhheakantuck* was what the Lenape called it, they told us in elementary school, with a curriculum's frank distance), disrupted and channeled east-west by barges steaming up to the Erie Canal or down to the westside ports.

Grand Central, flush, from tan marble to green tapestry, with air conditioning.

When the images subside, I think about the dispersal of time: how much was pointed uninhibitedly outward versus how much to myself versus how much to my screen.

I

I was heading home, the train streaming out of the Grand Central tunnel and up the 100s. When we crossed the first river, I pulled out my phone.

By Yankee Stadium I still hadn't touched it. I let the music play, the double-columned pause button dormant at screen's center as the prewars of East Harlem and the storage facilities and highways and small highway-side gardens of the South Bronx sat and negotiated meaning with the music. The meaning was – and always to my intention – broad, years instead of hours, as I looked out upon longstanding creations: Robert Moses's grand conceptions turned into stark, impressive, ugly, effective, problematic realities; residential blocks chalked full of diaspora, turnover, continuity, reimagination, remembrance.

When we got to the second river, the larger one, my fingers resumed management of the screen: fast choppy downward swipes, horse-length upward ones, thumbs converging to maximize, parting to minimize. The occasional stray lateral that did nothing, that was accidental, impotent.

We last spoke as I was getting off the train at Grand Central. I had been issuing uncertain advice. She was just beginning her summer-before-senior-year internship at a mainstay progressive think tank (nonprofits were the only point of reliable separation from the nascent administration), but on her second day she got a call of acceptance from an even more reputable organization.

She wanted to know if the internship would leave her enough time for the LSAT, for a 175 rather than a 165. I said that for her, it would. I believed it: her forceful will of direction, her abidance. Even over the phone she was rushing up to my squish-lipped rumination, butt-slapping, back-patting, getting it all to go faster.

I part, one heightened platform to another. Before me: Hastings-on-Hudson in black letters under a band of green. To my west, the river, silent and blue; the palisades, solid black, materially dull; the river valley empty, its dark streams in quiet estuarial compromise, barely moving.

White computer light beamed and filled the dark of the bedroom. Twelve tabs were open on the screen. A computer app rang, nautically.

A picture of Sarah appeared on the screen, tongue out with shin-low black spandex in the shadow of a western mountain. I propped up three pillows under my chest, my neck extending to the white. She came into view, the screen flowing through its dimensions rather than jumping image to image like a rhinoceros lining a corner's edge. She was similarly slouched in bed, black sweats, a pink tank top, her eyes focused tangentially, from me to what I imagine was her screen, her tabs.

I asked her about her day.

"Not as good as yours! Tell me about the city."

Just like any other day, I said. A subject of visitation, a reprieve (drink, food), an occasional moment of joy or thanks (though rarely one of special enlightenment), a warm affirmation, a return.

"And what of the job?" I asked.

She paused. "I think I'm going to take it."

"Shit yeah."

"It's not like I'm blowing up any near-term opportunity."

"My thoughts exactly."

"It's not like I'm short-circuiting an important experience."

"Butter. Cream. Please continue."

"It's not like I'm halting the acquisition of a skill set mid-stream."

"*Burning bridges*! You've yet to say *burning bridges*!"

"It's not like I'm commingling breakfast with dinner, shitting where I'm eating, trading dollars for pennies."

Our laughs coming and evaporating. I thought about my break from the world of self-strategy and whiteboard dialogue even as I was still tethered to it. That my foray into junk removal was only truly justified by my outlined one-year plan. All of which was undergirded by an economy – the conception of an economy - that didn't afford lapses, chasms in certainty, sabbaticals that weren't exiles to fancy schools abroad. An economy of finitude in which, via the natural and gravitational, the unpowerful or confused or disengaged bassineted downstream into jobs of self-preservation, comfort, limited scope.

"So you begin next week?"

"Probably the last week of June."

Another pause, my chin up, my bottom lip punched under my jaw.

"I think you should probably do it."

"I think I should probably do it too."

Tim Goodman awoke on the hottest day in June as three fans shouted across the room from one another at varying octaves and intensities. When he was done picking out a pair of clothes from a dresser as tall as him – he put them on, ever since his knee's demise, while sitting at the edge of his bed, at a speed subconsciously familiar – he walked the near football field across his family's long-owned property, released his shorts - his legs, to protect his knees, stayed buckled - and unveiled his gray pajama shirt.

Luridly, the day disclosed the coming season. One in which you could feel the pending 2 p.m. by how the sun pressed and breathed on the world; could feel how the heat trapped the low-lying blanket of black clouds from the previous sleepless night; could feel the humidity, its moisture seized from the woods and grass, from the pond's concentrated plentitude.

Now, hovering kidlike over bank's edge, Goodman recalled the chill of June, the water three months behind the sun. Too starkly contrary to the pending day to be welcoming.

But then: the submersion. The aquatic reorientation as the water rolls, stretches, curves. The wait as ninety-three degrees becomes sixty-seven (by August, that disparity is halved), his feet inclined downward near where the pond floor broke, his eyes planar with pads, clovers, striders, mayflies, somnambulant mosquitoes without target, sticks coated with wet pine tar; surficial supernumeraries that rise and shift noiselessly. The birds of the morning, a dove and, more intermittent, a chickadee, no longer cry in heat but sing in cold encumbrance. They, airbound, are still in the womb of the pond.

The right toes, six inches below the right heel, flex down into earth and thrust the heel into the air with the help of the calf, still muscular and propellant in its eighth decade. Chin and neck transition from water to air and back. Chest, shoulders and arms loosen as they too rise and fall, mostly still in water.

Movement – procession – in the softest of ribbons and strands.

He buckled his right knee toward his body as his left, erect, prodded forward and let go of the wet clay, his small, whiting hairs fully mopped and receded, his eyes open. He was now treading.

Back on earth. Towel to body, clothes to body, cane to hand…

Like a bagpipe blown to frontier, the aerobic metronome capable only of recycling energy already used, existent, the fumes of potentiality whiffing on every thrust to a shortening horizon.

His breaths kept shortening as he moved toward the house, his right leg dragging graciously, his left leg flexed, lifting, extending, contracting. He martialed his brain toward short strokes of discernment: the radius of the pond, the length of the field. He needed to walk that length before he could throw himself down into the shade of the living room.

He reached the slope near where the field became the front yard. Fervently, no longer gracious, he dragged his right leg up the small hill, its gradient steepening nearest to its peak. He rose until rise ended and dropped where the grass and stairs met, his legs' extant pond water pooling roundly on the wood, his back elevated by the jagged hypotenuse – four or so feet – between top and bottom stair.

A buzz through the seams of my black khakis.

I put the large, un-heavy box of comforters and linens down just in front of me and, none of my coworkers around, took my phone from my pocket. It was Dad.

He knew I was working, he said in his kind, beard-muffled, cigar-formal voice. But he had a question for me, which he asked.

"Sure," I responded. "The emphatic emailer."

Moments later I was out of the basement, where I had been storing and stacking boxes both familial and vestigial: old clothes, adolescent artwork, yearbooks, cassette and VHS tapes, landlines. Through the cellar door I entered a side yard between the house and garage. I stood off the garden path and opened my email to a forwarded message from a sender I didn't recognize.

Kevin,

He had a bad episode today. Nothing altered. Body still going. Mind well…

I noted the block phrasing, its lack of preface, its referentialism. Like they'd been discussing the matter episodically.

…Still, was struggling for breath after a swim. Collapsed on porch stairs…

Ella Goodman had only met Dad twice but liked him very much both times she did, as a friend of Tim's but also voluntarily, the way you do a person you like or admire free of all associations, who's done you the service of bringing you edifice or joy. And unlike her older brother's watery, untrustworthy community in the Berkshires, Ella found Dad to be proximate and likeminded in key ways, in ways her brother wasn't. He was reliable, unpresumptuous, polite, intelligent, and successful, softening the rock of life without turning it into a cloud. He was un-stubborn, a thought-and-taste-ful person who was also happy to embrace life's typicalities (offering up pictures of his kids on

22

his phone, submitting reasoned and true – if unremarkable – opinions on politics).

This is what Ella liked about him. She saw in Kevin and Tim a healthy asymmetry: a younger, successful Westchester inhabitant who had always maintained a real, sustained, if not always high frequency friendship with his older strong-willed friend who, since the days of their professional cohabitation at the United Federation of Teachers, had served the role of an advisor whose advice wasn't always taken (Dad leaving the world of public good – of, as Tim might call it, social democracy - for publishing was just one dimension of this); a pacified, disciplined and patient outward stance – the world of time abidance, pay raises – and its bold, less structured, more questioning antithesis.

… Then: he was fine. At least according to him as of ten o'clock this morning. I'm okay, he said. So I did what I always did: I suggested selling the house as we originally planned when he moved back up there 15 years ago. He said, Of course, that's why I'm here. I asked, Then why aren't you doing it. He mentioned something obfuscating, something about the house and its cumulative parts (he seemed delirious) – its rooms, things, history – to suggest breadth and enormity. You can't just rush-trash breadth and enormity, he said. I said we should have been thinking more actively then about this breadth and enormity back in 2003.

I could predict a lot of the houses I trashed prior to entrance, my casting admittedly quick, somewhat general.

And yet, in principle – as far as hierarchy, as far as priority – correct. A marriage of money and consciousness. Not terribly unlike my house: marble islands in the newer spaces, Arcadia rugs in the older ones, fragile wicker chairs that looked like they'd been transported from the gray clapboard of a Wellfleet veranda, free trade coffee, turnips, zucchini and spinach stickered with the origins of Dutchess and Columbia County farms; the artwork, passable originals, believable replicas: Rauschenberg, Craig Kauffman, an O'Keeffe Adirondack landscape; the records: Monk, Dylan, Verdi, The Talking Heads, Emmylou Harris, Prince.

In the basement, formerly valued artifacts became sunless and anonymous. The books, same words but depleted form, spat up dirt in your eyes, yellowed, smelled like old metal. The soft pages of the magazines contained piecemeal tears - top to hinge, bottom to fore. Old chairs and low-perched sofas became dusted quadrupeds of storage space, of air with a foundation.

The pianos, though, struck me most. Bosendorfers and Faziolis once shipped across the Atlantic that had been stripped of all sentimentality, keenness, usage, their keys pointed toward the raw dried plaster of the room's four sides, the square lumber back darkly pointed toward you like a turtle in water.

Past the driveway outside: cool asphalt; no traffic lines, the road a civil engineer's crown; lone streaks of sunlight where the canopy broke, beeches and hemlocks and maples wreathed over the road at nearly every aerial coordinate save for an orphan few. A damp sheet metal railing bent and curved with the dark gray, staving off a deep drop into deer and trail-laden forest where Labradoodles pranced and off-trailed with their owners, where trucks like ours housed passengers wearing uniforms, franchise-mandatory, fastening white cocoons that, when lit, puffed and reverberated around the cab's rectangle, between bored heads and into the glass-plated faces of iPhones and Androids.

One of the things I would tell our clients if given enough time, space and license – as I folded their clothes into trash bags – was that I was headed to London.

Why London, they would ask.

School.

Well, they would continue down the path I secretly hoped they'd follow (not just with them, but with myself, the type of ugly pretension that happily stays quietly patient, composed). A conversation more likely to be had the more north in the county you got, the more spacious and shaded the properties became. *What school?*

Flat-voiced, like I was off balance, like I farcically wanted to keep it in but was now obligated not to, I would tell them.

Sometimes my high school would also come up, often without my having even probed the topic. Like a sliding, spinning, functioning gadget. Sometimes I would point to a book, a couple of adjectives ready (doubly valuable if not about the book itself, but about the author). Often I said nothing at all, but even the way I spoke when I selectively did – the words, eyes, expression – suggested the polite concealment of a narrative twist, an intriguing life's chapter, a choice.

After the election people had kept saying there were two Americas. I heard it over and over again, cloyingly explanatory: in opinion pages, magazines. The observation was repeated in earnest – imbued words, frazzled minds, conceptions both proven and disproven – but shorn of any sign of familiarity. Efforts to glean in echoing, insurmountable darkness. Two people don't just spend a life vectoring at non-conjoining angles and, at a peremptory nation's beckoning, look back and see each other in full form.

The day before I left for the Berkshires I told my boss, who had already assigned me a truck for the following morning, that I wouldn't be showing up to work. That my previous day's work would be my last.

"No worries," he said, a prudent, indiscernible timbre on the tail of his voice. Like he had expected it and it had finally come. Like he didn't need a post-mortem about a vacation, an internship, the pending semester.

Kevin,

Don't feel the need to bring your boy up – if not as a spectator or friend. I had a shortness of breath, but I think that just means I was born in '44. I can't tread water for an hour anymore. These are my new, sad boundaries. But I don't think it signals anything exigent. My heart and lungs are, in my normal course of walking and breathing, fine.

I walk into a small stainless steel elevator, a mal-interpreted reflection standing before me in the metal. I press a plastic button, exit into the vertical stream of a hallway and angle into my seminar room about halfway toward a dead end, our seminar leader sitting there spectacled and bald and goateed, waiting, the toe side of his Grensons raised.

I am one of five members in the seminar. There is Vera from Cologne, Katharine from Taipei, Lydia from Turin. There is Abbott, the millionaire sixty-year-old Londoner who, upon selling his currency translation platform, sought a part-time degree as a cooldown before full-throated retirement.

I open my laptop, a book and an article printed onto quadruple-paged sheets. I know that I am likely the least read of the five on Bernanke.

More predictable: while everyone floats, slowly but fully, graf by graf, through the waterways of Bernanke's non-omniscient gold standard, I feel amply assertive – the result of confidence and limitation cohabitant – to balance out, Hegel-like, Vera's point A and Abbott's point B. *To weave and thrust us out of the muck of dutiful annotation; through the looming necessity of off-color, Ptolemical – but nevertheless historical – contention; through the patience (the nostalgia?) of historical gradualism.* (In a separate, less-sheened compartment I simulate the versions of me being perceived, the good ones - a participant humbly providing labor, banding together history so that others can magnify it – and the bad ones: an American glossing over all other times for *his* time, like a president in superficial conversation with an ally; a male in performative subterfuge, well-enough meaning but fundamentally defensive, self-congratulatory).

Vera interrupts. Not through direct condemnation but by wielding the explanatory function, the friendly, utile moniker of warring academia. I try answering her points in kind, but the further I go the more chaotic my point becomes. Abbott, assuming my ellipsis – dying words, pleading eyes – confirms us both, in equal proportion: diplomacy over correctitude. Lydia piggybacks.

Vera doesn't back away as much as she confirms her original point, much of what I said but, by my admittance, a bigger shape with less-defined corners; less aphorism, more poem.

Without any vocal sidestep or accent I agree, my smile, no longer constrained by a point unresolved – the uncertainty of two brains trying to trace the other – reaching out to where jaw meets ear.

The whole way up the Taconic Parkway I had my phone head down in the last of two coffee rings between driver and passenger, the very southern part of its face still visible. Not visible enough to see the name of the person trying to text or call but enough so that I could see the fact of such an occurrence, the metadata. I divided my gaze between the road and the half-visible face. I wouldn't touch it – it was unlawful, it was deadly – and so before turning the car on I made a Spotify playlist that would keep me driving.

I was wary but not near shiver, the way I had been earlier in the summer when I crossed the county to get to my assigned truck, or when I did errands, or even as I rode the traffic-devoid streets of Hastings.

While driving, the playlist got stale and I started changing songs intra-playlist, the phone elevated and just off my right eye so I could tensiously see both the road and phone. I couldn't help it. I searched artists more generally, for songs that would prod me somewhere deep or fun. I danced through and around and within them for those moments, 1, 2:36, 3:34, 4:00, adjusting volume, keeping my eyes on the road and the car in the lane with surprising proficiency, as the incident momentarily began to feel less like a lesson in categorical abstinence than one in strategic focus, location, ocular angle.

A brown decades-old Volvo sat box-shaped in the shade of two slender-limbed sycamores, their closer halves crossing and touching amid triangles and trapezoids of sky, cloud, light. In the trees' half-blotted aftermath stood the porch, upon which two logs sat between the doors and, on each log's outer flank, two rocking chairs. There was no railing. Everything on the porch had recently been coated in a colonial white. The door was open save for a politely creaking screen door.

From the porch the house's interior was the color of indoor dusk, one that blanketed chairs, rugs, desks, couches, bureaus, paintings and pictures with the exception of a ray or two of moving tangerine. What got hit was a matter of chance, a formula of sun and house: streams of oak floor, their color approaching cognac and walnut, rows of bookshelf, couch arms, a cast iron rack that hosted free-hanging fireplace utensils, the air itself, a medium of rolling and floating and tiredly-lit dust.

I took thirty steps left. The area south and west of the house was large, rhythmic, symmetrical, certain. Someone had once purchased and put money into the property and now it was either keeping or its old ailing inhabitant was working quite effectively to keep it. How? Did he bring someone in to the mow the lawn, to drag the canoes evenly onto the bank of the small manmade pond that had once been dredged and filled at the southern end of the property, to replace and reconfigure the rotting, damp-ening latticework - full red logs - of the pondside cabin, to orga-nize the family barn, a city family that had purchased the prop-erty mid-century and turned its tallest most spacious edifice into a back-office of relevant utility, cars, bikes (all flat), rusting and efflorescing tennis rackets, bare wooden golf clubs still in canvas bags, wiffle balls, baseball bats of wood, metal, plastic?

Or was this – against all physical encumbrances, against (even in the summer) light's temporal limits – him? Had *he* chosen to spend his time in such a positively Aristotelian manner, tending, maintaining, fixing, growing, cooking, preserving?

I was surprised, expecting, as I had, at least a conquerable form of mayhem. The mayhem in which the physically disabled and temperamentally eccentric exist and overcome. PhDs barely manage to maintain their apartments (open books, unwashed plate faces) let alone big properties, I thought. Not that Tim Goodman had degrees – according to Dad, he had dropped out of college. More that – and never for unjust reasons – it was my impression that much of the life of a person like that was focused on the aphysical. On war and *liberté*. On emotional and spiritual bankruptcy. On obscure local elections. On air rather than floor.

My nose is inches away from the window closest to the door. I shake the knob to see if it's unlocked. It is. But I don't go in.

I feel and hear a ring in my pocket. It repeats - a call. I take out my phone, look at the screen: *Sarah Abbott*. It is almost noon.

I walk toward the pond, where, when I arrive, I sit on a jumping ledge that extends from the side of the cabin, my toes two or three feet above the pond's surface, my phone still on the porch.

I had lied to Sarah when I picked up her call.

"Where are you?"

"A job. Way, way up north. Dover Plains. No service."

"Did you see my DM?"

"On Instagram?"

"Twitter."

"I haven't!"

I had, in fact seen it, from the small visual and textual representation I could decipher on screensaver without opening the file. Some blue-bannered publication. I asked if she had made a final decision on the internship swap.

"Texting my prospective new supervisor first thing in the morning."

I simulated through phrases that even weeks earlier I would have happily employed. *No sudden movements. Day at a time.* But the holes in my mental sieve had become smaller, less permitting.

"That's a great idea," I said instead, my voice eliciting distraction or, with the right ears, a practiced anti-irony. Nonreferential earnestness.

Josh,

*I saw on your website that you're currently searching for bloggers.
I'm not exactly sure what the greater designs of the position are –
whether you want a Tweeter, a conference-goer, etc. But, if none of
those things are necessarily determinative, I'd love to lend a hand.
I know how to use and read books. I know how to Google. And, as
you know, I have opinions.*

*When was our first interaction here? I could probably find out
by record but I haven't signed into that old account in years (not since
that website, which used to run everything, lost everything it ran
to this website). I gather it was the spring of 2008. Months before
the collapse. You were bunkered into an open-air office at some firm,
measuring bond products with a ruler. You were miserable. And
– no doubt in part because of your misery, your advantage – you
called it. You were a believer in recurrent history, in Popper, in the
inevitability of mal-humanity. You managed to dedicate adequate
time to both work and the blog, at least until the blog could be
monetized. So, a financial calculation, you opted for pseudonymity.*

*And I - a strange word to use for a person I had never met, who I
had merely just heard of - was really* proud *of you. JacobPeeWeeRiis:
the heartened flamethrower.*

The limp was naturally the first thing I noticed as he walked out to me, morphing into salience the closer he edged across the lawn, his walk reconciling the property's gradual but ongoing decline from the road toward the westward tree line. He walked, as I had, on a diagonal, relieving weight off the microscopic bruise on his right knee (through which a doctor in Pittsfield had politely and expertly drilled) by planting his left leg, the strong one, into the safe but strenuous angle of the hill.

He found it most effective to prod his right leg forward with centripetal motion: by heaving his calf with hip, butt and diagonal gravity and spinning it clockwise before allowing the calf to land of its own volition, flexing as it touched ground so as to pad the infirm knee, then using momentum from the prior twirl to commence the new one, again and again, slow, forward, his trunk in quiet, sturdy accompaniment.

I walked out to him, a light wave dialing over a toothy sun-compressed smile.

Within a hundred feet I noticed for the first time his smallness – slighter at least than I remembered. The entirety of his weight was now being held in the excess of his belly, which itself looked to be getting smaller, a river in desert, the hip bones making small tight indentations under his loosening skin, the skin appearing to have found meaning like wrinkles on an Arizona golf course. His clothes, therefore, were mostly too big for him. His shirts hung. His black large-pocketed jean shorts, sans suspenders, would have fallen and dragged, and with them they dropped far enough to reveal pockets of his gray briefs that ballooned with loose air; that started high because his butt started high.

Even his Tevas appeared long and tall, dragging and fumbling, airy, carrying and funneling when submerged in water.

Even more surprising was the greater lack of volume. That this was not the person I faintly recalled through telephone lines, whose email I was occasionally forwarded – even included on – whose atypical adamancy I had been introduced to like he was a holdover from some other prism, an era made ethereal by time, a Kurtz-like archetype that failed to encapsulate the figure of quietude and sartorial nonconcern that stood before me (part of that surely represented my own limits, and part of that my Dad's inability to capture to my limits a flesh-bound creation), brief and efficient, his smile seeking to shepherd strength and generosity through a weak body.

He sat me down on the wider of two couches in the living room, the loosely woven one (cotton and linen instead of microfiber), the one that could comfortably seat three people instead of two.

"Water? Beer?"

He still stood but peered down and forward the slightest half-inch, his weight on his vertically-planted cane.

"Sorry?"

"*Do you want a drink?*" he repeated, abandoning his regimen of vocal efficiency, smiling. I asked what he had.

I took in the house while he was in the kitchen. *Balance*, I again thought, as I did when I first gazed upon the totality of the property. New England's plain clothes and square brick, its sub-surficiality - intellectualism, religiosity, verbal fluorescence - its humble utilitarian efficiency, its mulled non-elaboration.

The western United States' vibrantly colored landscapes painted dreamlike onto canvas and paper and panel, a diversity of carbonic origin: animals of a dignified glory and self-suggested gravity – rams, buffalo, black hawk – water-retentive shrubbery, sunbaked mud, deerskin, cowhide, denim, leather.

On the stretch of wall just above the front door and below the ceiling were a chain of stick figures, half-hashed and jovially strewn but, like Matisse, strangely shapeful. They danced where the perpendicular planes met, similar sizes but with different postures, shades, base design. Some were lightly colored, others the incandescent but unclear color of dark mercury. Some had candles for heads. Some had wider planted legs. Some had arms that were raised vertically, in near proximity, to the ceiling. Silently (the photograph's perpetual mystery) they moved, in opposite directions, in angles, in varying closeness and distance. But they were all going, bending, rising, falling. All had air within and between them.

Other emblems of the miscellaneous (and, how I so saw it, of balance, though others could have as easily described it as unpredictable, a Markov sequence): an artificially colored picture of Count Basie, white-suited and whiskered, downward-peering, his mouth pressing obliquely on a cigar; a monochrome of Ted Williams sternly holding his bat, loose but confident; Ella Fitzgerald, hair cut to a buzz above her temporal bone, a masterfully incongruous perm eaving just over her left eye; a discerning Eleanor Roosevelt, her lower lip barely parted from teeth, leaving open the possibility of a smile, a good day; a Duchampiam bicycle wheel, wooden, hanging just above the fireplace in the stead of a gold-plated ancestor.

We went to a Mexican restaurant in Lambeth that sold ten-ounce Sols and overpriced guacamole and had a cute steel spiral staircase that extended graciously into a basement, where we found the only available table in the restaurant. It was never positively a date. We had met at a kitchen party, one of those gatherings where twenty students crowd into free blank space to drink canned ciders and plastic-bottled alcohol before eventually, once consumed, going out to a pub or (unlike in America) a club.

By the following day I had nothing but memories of fog and fondness. She was born in Shinjuku and moved to North London when still young. Her parents had since moved back to Tokyo, but she was still here. She studied international governance. Calm brown eyes, round nose and face, white teeth, beautiful wavy lips colored hot pink.

The following Saturday we were touching shoulders in Borough Market. We both donned faded jeans of different grays, hers blacker. She had on boots, leather and laced, and I, red Sambas. Uncertain but not doubtful, we voyeured sushi, curries, vinegar-soaked injera, tiramisu, a barbeque pulled pork stand that had the full pig on display, eyes gauged and spindled onto its back, forcing her into a grimace, a gasping, laughing breath of exasperation.

We got to the end of the line with our prandial napkins and started walking west, along the river.

The spiral staircase is immediately off my left eye. For the first time in our three encounters, I ask about her parents.

"Banking" (I liked this. Something about calling it *banking*, raw, dumb and true, rather than *finance* or *investment banking* or *i-banking*), she says. Her Mom was the especially successful one. The one that had been asked to come over. The *MD*.

I asked what bank, to which she provided one of five or so answers I was expecting.

"Never heard of it," I said, to which she laughed as she scraped guacamole from the granite onto a lightly salted chip, the bowl languid and un-echoing.

"Where are you?"

I was trying to decipher the Wi-Fi password, which Tim had handed to me on a crusty sheet that Verizon gave him whenever it was they originally came to install the Wi-Fi (probably at Ella's bidding). He added that he didn't really use it. The only internet communication with which he engaged was emailing. That was where he spent all his web time, even more so than reading news, which, even in winter, he got boomeranged onto his front steps.

His emailing took place fourth thing in the morning, after food, news and swimming, on a big desktop downstairs, a barely twenty-first century iMac with a glossy buffed up exterior, candy-colored. It was huge, built into thin plaster through which Goodman had cut a hole so that the device's router, modem and Ethernet could connect from the ground to the wall.

"In the bathroom."

"In which of the earth's billion bathrooms are you in?"

Minutes earlier I told Tim that I needed to retire, carrying the Wi-Fi information with me to the bathroom where I had been trying but failing ever since to get onto Vandermeer247. The Wi-Fi, rather than display a check mark, kept encircling clockwise in small black pellets. And so I would return to settings, put the whole apparatus in Airplane Mode, wait ten seconds, drag the bubble back to green and re-input the password.

I tried putting Sarah on speaker.

"Family visit."

"With your parents?"

"Well…" I stopped inputting. I pursed my eyes, trying to find the apt explanation.

"Dude, where are you?"

"I'm so sorry."

"*Where are you?*"

"I quit my job."

Shera,

I think you've been spared a couple of the major tendencies.

> *One tendency: I rarely ever see you bored. I certainly never did when we worked together. I can still picture that hunched fast walk that made you 6'1" instead of 6'3", that made the three hairs that still exist on your head move.*

> *You could probably sell that dimensional sense of meaning for $100 a jar. Surely it comes from fleeing Gujarat in the 90s (when the SOB that now runs the whole place used to run that specific place), when young adulthood brought your pre-9/11 idealism to a floor in Woodside and a roving cab, when your intellect and the State-sanctioned reward of a longer stay brought you into CUNY and later into the manila-colored mediocrity of the New York City Department of Education, when, by the time the towers did come down, you were well into career and family, beyond even cartoon nativism.*

> *Will boredom be on your horizon? Certainly your kids'. When it comes, you will know. You will feel it. You will find yourself taking up sports. You will turn to music - how music is the great savior of the bored mind. You will find yourself downloading apps, looking up directions to zoos, venturing down to Comedy Clubs.*

> *For now, I implore you: please keep reading Al Jazeera and the BBC.*

To the Boston Globe:

An even-handed editorial you wrote about the passage of Poppy Bush for the most part, but one fundamental error.

You state that Bush's 1988 campaign "made much of Willie Horton, *convicted first-degree murderer" who committed a slew of violent crimes while on furlough.*

The error you repeat is that you fail to mention that the criminal was never known as "Willie" until the Bush campaign chose to rename him for the purposes of their ad. He'd always been known as – and was - William Horton.

We ate dinner at the onset of dusk on the porch's two firm-backed armchairs, the door between us. We were like a TV dinner-eating couple, but in the stead of a program we looked onto a lightless, shaded, quiet road from which the sun had already departed.

Dinner: small, well-done cheeseburgers from a saucer-shaped charcoal grill that resided under a shade tree in the house's back field; an oil-doused, thin-cut medley of green pepper and white onion, blackened by smoke and grate; halved cobs of corn.

He forked his vegetables carefully, turned the burger upside down so that his hard palate got the thinner bun and his lower mouth the airy potato roll, mayo, cheese, tomato. He rocked steadily. The chair, when halting back down, made a single dying pitch with the stone surface, transonic enough to time his revolution from peak to trough. His legs were hairless, raised; beneath his calves they were browning and ironing. His feet were more expressive, vibrant, sanguineous: soft violet in the dusk, livid pink in the sunlight.

"Can I bring anything in?"

Tim was eating one of his last epicentral bites. Neither of his eyes nor brows popped at my suggestion. Like he hadn't heard my question, or was unaffected by it, or had heard it but practiced uncommonly central control of his inner and outer levers of perception (they worked on their own timetables, for the selective purposes of his intrigue).

Minutes later I was relocated to the couch I had sat on earlier as Tim soaked and parsed dishes in the adjoined kitchen to my right, washing the cookware first, allowing the aluminum butts to moisten in shallow pools of bubble and remnant pepper and oil. He moved on to plates, glasses. The smaller, narrower ones he shot with a turkey baster to loosen unitary particles – coffee stains, sugar blots, plate-adherent foods. When he cleaned the silverware, the spigot, set too high, caused brief but forceful streams of water to ricochet off the metal and sponge and onto his large, overhanging chambray.

Live with me and *hang out* and *not to worry* were the only answers I ever really derived from my offers to help him in activities for which I was more than qualified - as was any adult - his (almost romantic) bid for self-sufficiency splayed largely and openly before me. Typically, such a stance would have suggested to me that I wasn't welcome – I had been summoned by family, actual and proverbial, to be a caretaker, an aid, a support mechanism, and to those titles I was, from the one person who seemed to not have a say in any of it, quite explicitly not permitted. But nothing else about his attitude or decorum did. He housed me quite graciously, showed me to my room, tried to help me with my bags when I first arrived before I warded him off and brought them up the stairs myself - albeit to the room to which he directed me.

I'm glad you're here was the other thing he kept saying, and though quite simple I felt like I could read small valleys of tone and subject in his words. It almost reminded me of something he would have said to Dad - brotherly.

Less over more. Quiet over din. Availability over business. Time. Space.

But how hard space really is when you enter between its walls. The hope to see over them, the hopelessness of failing to grow to such heights, suffocating you in your chair, prompting you to pause the game, whip out your phone, open the door, pour a glass, walk downstairs, plug your ears, arrange a date, call a friend. You twitch (your body only realizes this once all other noise has been turned off). A movement of the arm. An adjustment of your chair. A pressing of the feet. An oddly syncopated pooling of oxygen in the throat. A scratch.

Her name flanked a small green circular icon signaling availability, her virtual presence.

Calling… In my background, a gold-shaded reading lamp, creamy pillows, headboard, the room's drab tan light. On the wall opposite the windows hung a humbly framed painting of a commercial schooner, embattled under heavy clouds but a calmer dusk nascent in the distance. Things seemed busy, even turbulent, but typical and without panic.

Calling… She was prancing down a Washington thoroughfare, feet moving, arms bustling, head adjusting.

"You quit your job?"

"Are you walking-and-talking me?"

"Didn't I tell you? I'm the new Deputy Chief of Staff!!!!!!!!"

"Of the White House?"

"Universe."

"Yes, I quit my job."

"Why?"

"Don't matter. I'll subside."

"Subsistence the new goal, eh?"

"For now."

"You really have caved to the 'spirit of 48."

"*For now.*"

"For how long?"

"Protracted."

"Why?"

I told her shrouded, shaded truths. "A family favor."

"So if up to you, you'd still be bungy-cording sleeper sofas?"

I lied. "Yes."

"And when you're done with the family favor?" A question that especially bothered me given that she knew I'd be in London in three months.

"The world is my oyster. Landscaping. Pyramid scheme. Ice cream commerce."

She laughed.

"Or," to my angrily satirizing surprise, "Even more horrific. Teacher."

Sarah stopped on the thoroughfare. "Not funny. My aunt is a teacher."

"So is mine."

"But I want to just clarify," she said. The camera was now level, revealing the bottom of the city's square, height-capped buildings.

"Sarah…"

"Is that somehow a reference to me?" she said, her voice now straight, contralto.

"Not a one."

"That I'm trying to be *better than*?"

"I'm just saying that I'm *OK*. Fed, visible, grid-bound."

Very quickly we untangled ourselves from our misunderstanding, Sarah offering one or two more clarifications on teachers, odes to their greatness, effortful, which she wouldn't have made if she hadn't felt something, if she didn't feel proximate to what I did, powerful in its inexplicability.

I said nothing more. There was something on the tip of my tongue about time optimization – how I needed to be less certain of it, less focused on it – which, seemingly the beginnings of a crusty, faux-novelistic declaration, I dropped.

I tried my best to keep my phone off before the sun went down. Mainly this was an exercise in endurance. I would turn the device head down when I was done using it in the evening, go to bed, wake when I woke – without an alarm – roll to my right and, without consulting the window-side nightstand on which the phone lay, walk downstairs.

This was difficult for reasons of habit as well as network. I had to tell everyone in my orbit that I'd respond to them in the evening – calls, emails, group texts, Facebook messages, Facetimes, captioned pictures, forwarded articles, DMed memes. At first it felt palpably defiant, then abstractly defiant, then – fully adjusted – undefiant, then preferred. I felt more energetic, more observant, more wakeful, more generously able to offer my most precious units of value: time, energy, thought, take.

As the first week of my stay came to an end I found myself walking down the stairs just after seven, and even then I'd be pouring coffee that had already soothed, Tim having lidded the stove pot an hour earlier. The living room would be empty, and I'd pour two small cups of temperate coffee, top them with two percent, place them proportionally in the microwave and then usher my body and the porcelain out through the grass, under the smell of pine needle and onto the dock, where I sat, gazing out at a pair of thinning white arms held over a noodle, weighing it down, smoothly rolling and drowning the foam before allowing it to return to the brown surface.

One morning he leaned his left arm over the noodle, gesturing to me with his right.

"Sorry," I responded. "Don't really swim."

Goodman flailed his arms freely and boyishly over the flotation device, a signal of protest, his pits huddled forward so that the noodle would catch them, the water stretching and huddling familiarly, splashes big enough to imply uncontroversial disorder. Bourgeois improv: the dada of Buzzards Bay, the Delmarva Peninsula, Maine lagoons.

He then paddled, breaststroked, and, eventually, crawled – his body in an aquatically bolstered handstand - to where the grass hit the sandbank. He lifted himself to the grass and sat down, his legs resting outwardly, his bathing suit loose and shapeless, hanging from his lower waist to just below his knees.

I watched him in this posture from behind, wondering if his transition from water to land suggested a return, latent and oncoming, of his condition. I didn't ask, but his breaths – ballooning out into the still-free epidermal space of his compressed center, soft and visible – suggested a continuation of mind, muscle, organ and bone.

He turned around and pointed vaguely to the half-hidden edifice behind me. I followed his hand to what I already knew existed, preparing to help him up (another act for which he accepted minimal assistance) so that he could begin his soft limp back across the field, but instead he asked me to open the cabin door, rolling himself from butt-down to fetal to biped, through the shade of the pines, onto the wet platform and into the smaller of two compartments, a storage unit full of bright colors and innocuity - piles of noodles, hulas, aquatic recliners, terrestrial lawn chairs rusting at their knees, toys, flattened beach balls, sand utensils, animal-shaped sponges - and then through a doorless passageway into a larger, mostly empty but nonetheless kept room, its floor and walls made of rosewood planks. To the passageway's immediate right was a waist-high solitary black furnace with a spiral silver handle, non-conductive, and across from the furnace were two sitting platforms, butcher's pine, stacked one atop the other, the higher one upon which I took a seat, bent toward the black steel pit as Tim sorted a small stack of wood in the corner, small enough to fit into the fixture's glass-encased corridor and from which it would depart in a newer freer form.

After dinner I would take a walk by myself, the opposite direction of my walk with Goodman earlier in the day, where, instead of going up the hill that went southward from his house, I would go down the hill, northward, to where the dirt road turned paved (to where it met the yellow lines) near the intersection of Routes 20 and 22. There I would sit in a marsh of overgrown and sometimes moistened grass, its view hidden from the main road but visible from Vandermeer, looking east toward the bugless distance, toward Massachusetts.

One view I would focus on in particular, like I would have to recall it, was toward a lone hill in the relative northwestward direction of Williamstown, sharp-rising, conical, a bald indentation on its left slope. There it sat, tall and odd, autonomous, undeveloped, constant, expansive, inanimate, profound, limited. Unacknowledged but for my rambling interiority.

An unexpected division in expectation. On the one hand, total asymmetry: the beaten Keds, the Red Sox hat (the bill beginning to stream cloth but still principally whole), the flannel that hung save for two soft-peaked crests near his chest and stomach where it tautly hugged, the overhanging jeans. It was hard to find things that fit with his sub-waist, a freelance of body: short legs, narrow pelvis, wide thighs, lean calves, small feet. None of which he cared to hide because he had neither the vanity nor sartorial wit nor lack of confidence. Not that he was cocky, but he also wasn't *not* cocky, his whole persona centering around an intuitive, nonverbal sense of present conviction, whole enough for him to wear with strength over his clothing.

When he wore, he therefore wore with commitment – without shadow, angle or condition. People saw him and experienced him. He evoked – his memory, his humor, his unexpected turns of seriousness, fast-coming and disorienting and which almost seemed to be asking for an exemption, a citation.

This was the root of the symmetry, one that was willed by a healthy sense of declaration despite tension, a fearless attempt at celebreality under-bellied by a very basic tautology: that *he* understood (as anyone should), however unextraordinary, however small, the legitimacy and reality of his own presence and speech; that he knew, hinted at by certain junctures of the face - though his words couldn't yet encapsulate it - that all of it was a fleeting and soon to be distant amalgamation of flowing limbs and words, the polite maneuvering of office furniture in what would be a decades-long succession of life. A Mobius strip of reality, curved but intermittently perceptible. A grid of succeeding possibilities, protracting and fading.

Is this what the man across from him saw? His hair began just before the top of his head, as if it were using the upper forehead as a vallum against a fast-approaching exogenous force: rain, a playfully thrown dodge ball. Reputation and fame were aging his hair into gray, though it almost looked to be blonding, fast converging with his milky-lidded future grandkids, fast approaching the uniform white clapboard and green shutters of northwest Connecticut. His facial features near-unitarily fared in different thematic directions. His forehead, large and Roman, hovered over hazel, stately, unblinking, small-slotted eyes. His ears were pointed. His nose was narrow and curved, the tip and dorsum peering, swanlike and Calabrian-shaped, over the columella. His chin was pared back and square. His mouth, a humble gateway, clothed, until someone was deft enough to stir him, a far more descriptive set of tall protruding white teeth.

They began to discuss reasons for appointment. Goodman knew him only to be a faculty member and prolific writer and, yes, a conservative. But he was an adamant heart – not by fact but by impression – floating in pedal leather, loose khaki and Oxford cotton (he wore them like they were pajamas) over the room's quieting, calmly expressive rug. They sat in tan chairs with chubby hovering backs and convex leather stools. A skeletal knee-high end table separated them.

It was on the front of Goodman's chair just under his left hamstring that he noticed a plaque, a stitching, the color and shape of a medallion. The stitching suggested a present or an award but said nothing of title or achievement, its only manifestation a trio of splayed initials: WFB.

But ubiquity is ambiguity, a fact which he kept being reminded of in the high-ceilinged room in which they sat, the relics about what he expected: pictures of the family surrounded by the steel, stone and glass of a city that birthed but did not embrace them (at least not in idea or intention); book and magazine signings; schools of young fair-haired men with clean necks huddled over their suits in concert to an unenumerated something; a picture of Buckley embracing a man with diagonally bent eyes who Tim recognized through Mom's family, whose tenure, along with several other prestigious families of historic Yale, the family had vehemently fought against: Willmoore Kendall.

It occurred to Tim that Buckley very well knew his family, had maybe even exchanged letters of puffed-up, unactionable disapproval with them, endemic within an institution like Yale, the activist faculty member versus the activist alumnus. It stirred a reflective thought: had he not inherited the name of his father's family of humble educators, he might not have been afforded the company.

"I would like to become a writer," Goodman eventually said after minutes of palaver, truthful to the content of his self-summons, but... Well, writers write. They also report. They advertise. They write policy, law. They write for screen. They write for stage. Ubiquity is ambiguity.

Buckley's face had not changed shape or stature since Tim had prompted, jeered, admonished, complimented him, first about *God and Man* – jokingly, Goodman asked, like it was a moth problem, if the Communists from within had been dealt with as programmatically as they had originally entered, driving into gothic New Haven on the interstate from Ethel and Julius' living room – and then, more heavily, more ferociously, about "Why The South Must Prevail."

Peevishly, Buckley smiled as if at the crazed man who rode the A from Inwood to Idlewild, who just so happened to wield the gift of poetry, the punchline. A smile that left ample space in his cognitive tent for authorial judgment and open-mindedness (someone too judgmental is a jerk; someone too open-minded is a heart-wrench, a bore), the dull mouth giving way to the intriguing teeth, the eyes stately and remote but eventually arriving to the fore like a tennis player at net, the chin tucked back seat-like.

"Journalistic or belletristic?" he asked.

Tim's heart sunk into his seat the way gravity – whether as metaphor or encountered force – muffles and sinks levitous hope. His body appeared to be calm but was tensely operating. He grimaced to hide his inner storm.

Belletristic.

He had never heard that word. Should the ethnic-verbal-intellectual multiverse of Cambridge have taught him? Was it an abdication, a function that hadn't been acquired on one of the city's thoroughfares, in one of its fence-painted summer backyards with stone steps and a well-tailored garden; in one of its Christmastime living rooms full of Jell-O cakes and devilled eggs and small helpings of coronation chicken; in the schools; by his very parents, educated – unlike him and grandpa – at the city's most famed and glorified institution?

But wait, his brain now pivoting back toward the threat and possibility of the word, throwing out the last three syllables as it wound the first in legerdemain. *Belle, belle.*

"Belletristic," said Goodman.

Buckley's eyes maintained their quarter inch of diameter, the only sign of applause or impression or curiosity or amusement coming from his nose down.

He sat on a tan cement staircase on Prospect Street within a calm gray autumn zephyr. He smoked a cigarette. He thought.

He was happy to have had walked up the stairs. He had felt no judgment, nor the stuffy un-fun of golf course conservatism he'd worried about. He could still hear the voice – stilted, siloed, lispy. He could still see the face, reflective (though on more than just an occasion he over-believed in people) of a fascination less typical, less Doric, less deciduous, less suburb-green.

A world slightly less than square, one that would continue to lose its edges, its straight lines…

He didn't back away from that world. He knew – no, he *felt* - it would bud merely by the way people talked to one another, in the soul and cynicism and discernment they orphaned around. He felt it would gestate, be born, develop, cultivate. He felt it would walk and talk and dexterously pry and parse and edify and wonder and inspire and stir and alienate. He felt it would be neither accepted nor stopped. He felt it would become an *it*, a rolling, folding, shrinking, ballooning force that would be inherited, mocked, subverted, fixated on, borrowed from. That even amidst its subjugation the competition would watch its movies, read its books, see its shows, listen to its music, buy its tickets, hoist its *physicale*, explicate its ink.

Our accommodations were dispersed throughout the city because student accommodation requires ordinance, law, exemption, advocacy (little us, beating private equity with our single beds, our desks, our built-in bathrooms). Choosing grounds for communion was therefore a game of mapping, tube lines, addresses, inquiries of scheduling. Some nights we'd get invited to a flat, others we would go out and, when out, drink and take advantage of our contrived diversity: East Coast and West Coast and South Coast American, Asian-Australian, Chinese, Indian (though she had gone to college ten minutes from my house), French, two German – leftist from Bonn, libertarian from Frankfurt – the awkward, fun, ever-reliable Andalusian (he spoke the worst English but his smile, diastema, his Strokes and Joy Division t-shirts and his grades, the best in our group, compensated for it), the Mexican, white but proudly Latin, handsome and bearded, critical, sharp, serious.

We talked: transnational taxation, racism, Anglo and Anglo-American centricity, imperialism. Far enough from campus so that the Wetherspoons employees knew we belonged to a university without having to know which one. The din and tacky silver and bronze and flare and catch-phrasing and campaign pins and placemats of the chain experience surrounded us, the menu made of nachos and burgers topped with burnt sugar and four-quid Amstels. It mollified our sternness. I kept myself to a five-drink minimum: twenty pounds. This was the limit I designed for myself, the yardage between drink five and six only hard to endure momentarily, until I waited for the conversation's declarative and anti-declarative paragraphs to complete, hugged bodies, cupped hands, paid my tab and entered the evening rush, where, even without a host page, words and fragments both shitty and poetic began to shorten and expand and reorganize.

To the Times-Gazette,

Should I apologize? Well, I will, given the nature of this correspondence. I'm sorry the jobs that were going weren't ones being done on a big double-screened desktop on a twentieth floor. They weren't ones where advisors advise other advisors. No. They were ones featuring hands, feet, jeans, hats.

But about that *hat? The blood-colored one which your paper recently endorsed: I don't see bellicosity as much as I see terror. I see a young person looking around nervously, like the former schoolmate who went to college and who writes annoying but probably true social media posts approaches around the corner. I see an older person in sunglasses, confused, quiet, reticent, carrying him or herself around polite and wary in case someone tries to rob them of their very brain, balance, goodness.*

All of which comes back to maintenance. *A plea for vision at sunset. For a contained, thin, un-curious and perhaps selfish version of beauty, truth.*

Believe it or not I actually passed through your small Ohio town once. I was on my way back to New Mexico, where I lived at the time, from Massachusetts, and on my way from Columbus to Cincinnati (and, from there, to Louisville, Nashville, Memphis…). But the road through Dayton was being repaved. From the highway you could see nothing, no water tower, no diner, no movie theater, no school, no library, no church – though through the magnolias I knew there to be bipeds. I knew there to be an utterly devout preacher, an omnivorous librarian, an efficient contractor, a humorous clerk, a righteous elected official, an amorous parent and, most importantly, children of a fate undecided. I knew there to be the rudiments of democratic interaction — curiosity, earned decency. Like the surrounding forest, I knew there to streams of sunlight.

Do you still have a library? Many of the small towns surrounding me no longer do. And what are the confines of your town? A block? Half a block? A store?

To Berkshire Community College:

Before getting sick I built walls, statue foundations, park benches and other stone-based structures. I was, in my ascendant retirement, a stone mason. I thought of it as a retirement job, but really it just became my new job. And before every summer I'd go around to the area high schools and I'd recruit juniors and seniors less interested in tests than in work. I looked closely, carefully sought out what I realized morphed into the similar archetypes, with many of them overlapping: the solemn-faced, sparse-worded, hat-wearing, wholesome son of a solemn-faced, sparse-worded, hat-wearing, wholesome Dad; the boy of misplaced energy, *full of vibrancy and possibility but with no sense of measure or compartment; the boy who's been failed, ferociously intelligent but not in ways measurable by school (a learning disability undiagnosed), or from an area where there's not enough money, infrastructure or human capital to parse through to the seams of gold and velvet; the asshole of carbonic existence who makes you pray for early September; the kid who doesn't want to be there, or doesn't belong there, and who you lamentably had to meet in such a context; the kid who you pity because you know that this — shelter, food, drink, stone — could well be their life.*

Most of those boys are somewhere between their late 20s and late 30s by now. I'm sure the vast majority would greet me. Fuck, I would make them, look them in the eye until they saw me and shed that brittle tight-chested look and low-pitched affect that men often give to other distant men (for perspective's sake, my voice is two octaves higher, almost John McCain-y), bring to their mind something funny or less serious that happened to them, to us.

I speculate upon my actions partly because I did in fact see one of them recently. He was one of the quiet wholesomes. The type that drove the family car – and well - the second he was licensed. I saw him at Home Depot and he came right up to me, beating me at my own extroverted strategy, bending close enough so that his hat's white stitching was six inches away from my shoulder blade. He spoke in the same warm, congenial, complete sentences and gnomic aphorisms that one imagines in the mouth of a good Southern boy, simplistic but, from a certain angle, plenty to live by. His truck had his last name printed just beneath the door handle, branded in the clear serif of a small business. Two pieces of foot-wide plywood arced out of his bed (sitting in their shadow were a couple of stray jerry cans, tilted and dispersed like they were empty, the weight of air). He shook my hand and departed for his truck, where he shuffled the plywood into familiar formations before he made way for a moving car to which he waved like one does to a car that suddenly reveals an animate connection.

One morning we got into his car and didn't return until later that evening. It was the first time I saw Goodman in what amounted to full dress: cargo shorts, Tevas (his knee characteristically bare, unwrapped), a safari hat, a short sleeve plaid shirt, a black fleece vest. Where we were headed was unclear. Goodman drove (a function to which, of course, I repeatedly offered my capacities) as I sat passenger in mesh shorts and ankle socks, an idle 210 pounds.

Beneath my millennial conception of the laissez-faire ("he's just doing him"), I wondered if I was doing my job by listening to him or if I wasn't doing my job by acquiescing. Was my behavior truant, neglectful, wishful, lazy, passive? Was I allowing an imperiled man the right of reckless agency just because he carried with him certainty, because he viewed himself the way that perhaps many old people do: as a thing to be used and deployed rather than protected?

The highway's asphalt-colored entrance ramp had bends and inclines that from a distance reminded me of recreation: a park slide, a roller coaster, a hamster tunnel. Curved and soft and un-controversial. The cars too. How they move. They don't even move – moving is an act of deliberation, an overt acknowledgment of dispensation – as much as they *slide*, their movement constant, magical, limbless, sourceless.

Was this coincidence? Or was it all a form of *trvializing the drop*? All that is fun and fast and expeditious mapped onto a captured world, masking speed and distance with seamless functionality, placidity. Masking the violent coagulation of oil and and heat with exhaust and water and cruise control. A regime of revving, of silent acceleration.

I was coming home from DC, passing through the brief dwindling expanse between Philadelphia and New York until the suburbs started reintroducing themselves near Brunswick, continuing up I-95 until I began to straddle the island with the cops and firefighters and secretaries - whose separation from mainland New Jersey almost seems manmade, a meek strait separating them - and, upon hitting the Meadowlands, found myself between and among the stacks, their amber-tipped chimneys coloring and sewing the evening sky with ephemeral gas. It was late spring. The cars surrounding me were driven by and chauffeuring tee-shirted people through the indispensable vehicular artery of the Boston-Washington megalopolis.

Then, over my right shoulder, a plane, its mass and sound descending and disappearing into Newark.

And, eventually, the stacks still partitioning my vision, I saw the other island. I pick out Wall Street's first visual signatures, remote, the curved indentations and soft stains of the buildings from the wires and scaffold and rust and concrete and gas surrounding me.

Jerusalem and the mills.

I peer over my seat to supplant the brown vinyl fencing that separates highway from industry, seeking to glimpse the island of everyone, everything, power.

Until: a car, several yards before me and to my right and moving decidedly leftward even before turning on its blinker.

Dumbass, I think, expecting it to acknowledge its surrounding proportions and pick up speed, make diagonal haste. But it doesn't. It is right under me, ten feet maybe, with a two to three mile an hour speed deficit, and so I too make a sharp left, into the third of four lanes, hoping to slalom into a rightward before carrying on, vertical and parallel. But when I reorient into the penultimate lane the steering wheel won't stabilize. It jukes back and forth indeterminately. I keep moving straight and left, the wheel shuffling on a thirty-degree dial as I attempt one last sharp rightward into the fast lane. This is where the left axel brakes. And where the axel brakes, the entire thirty-five-hundred-pound creation inherits all movement and momentum, up, around and over its left side, gliding, flipping, falling, puncturing. In nightmares I can still feel myself part of a greater omniscience. A formula often attributed to God but in this case a formula of bureau, management and consumer law. Misuse, indulgence, endangerment, the endangerment caused by other drivers, the enterprise's inherent danger – of going speeds that will bruise and tear and break and incapacitate – is metered down to where the fingers have no space between them, is baked into the price of the car; the sound of calculation and foreknowledge, of fatherly corporatism if the ramparts keep you from the bone-jarring road and of hard-hearted self-absolution, of lawyering up, if they don't.

But nowhere in the experience exist the sounds of panic. Modernity's most singular and statistically common horrors happen too quickly. And because there exists none of those traditional triggers – an alarm, the braying of a sentient scream – and because you are alone, the experience is an utterly quiet one.

II

I recalled something a professor had quipped to me – the type whose confidence had besotted his humility, who didn't read as much as he used to - as I was walking down the Kingsway's slight incline toward school. It had a scholar's caveat: this is an organism indented with impression and experience, not scholarship. With the long, loopy, melodic intonation of an isle native.

It had to do with the original families of the isle, which, through conquest and concession – the Britons, Britannia, the Anglo-Saxon settlement, the Vikings, the Norman invasion and, like a sinister favor returned, the Brits' many invasions abroad – had managed a dual sorting and diversification: houses, blood, appearance – inheritance.

My back tilted toward school and the river, my body fluid and unmarred, I would test this theory by the momentary representation of passing faces.

I saw similarities – the slightly altered recreations of people I knew, the lips and noses and eyes of people I knew by representation, fame (I would double check their faces online when I got to class). I mapped familiarities. I tested the pretense and possibility of descendancy.

But soon it got too variegating, too circumstantial. How, for instance, was I to know that bubbly cheeks, small eyes, pronounced lips and conspicuous eyebrows were shared by fact or by inheritance? What if they were shared by basic arithmetic, by the parsimony of features, by biology's few and countable variations?

But it was more than that – and to this realization I thought back to home, its very settlement founded on an unspoken but clearly transmitted conception of *frontiers*, supremacist exclusion, of whites staying white, that had been taken from here.

The blessed irony being that the very idea had become more impossible by the year, was, after centuries of half-success, failing speedily. This irony I'd experienced in full view growing up in cabs and stores and stands and hospitals and stadiums and civic halls. The names on class lists: Colon, Radigan, D'Allesandro, Patel, Wang, Abboud, Brodsky, Boateng, Smith.

The same eye with which I currently saw the thoroughfare. New faces. New words. New thoughts. All flexing the same functions – hip, thigh, calve – up toward High Holborn.

Sitting on my desk: my phone, the carrier of my recent conversations with Dad and Ella: Dad's conversations effortful, told in a small, solemn, poignant 10-font Rockwell (typewriter chic); Ella's less structured but temperamentally reassuring, slangy, sprightly, confident. At select moments I can hear Tim's authoring: similar laugh, similar narrative pivoting. The phone sits on the bottom left corner of the rectangular blockwood like Tierra Del Fuego on a flat map.

Visible on the laptop is a tab featuring Goodman's email, darkening with the day, the password of which I had been given permission to access by Mountain View the prior summer.

His writing, half-helpful, which I had found in a heavy rusted set of forest green cabinets in his basement, sits to the laptop's right in vertical succession, rectangles and perpendicular rectangles and diamonds.

"I just want to clarify," Sarah said to me right before Tim and I got in the car.

"SA, you don't have to clarify." I was surprised. I thought we had already made our clarifications and retractions the last time we spoke.

We had begun the conversation how we usually did: verbal elongations, accenting, yawning. We exchanged predictabilities.

"No temporal judgment. No professional one. No status one."

"Of course," I said, with the affect of a particular place and time, the transmogrifying possibility of a *dude* lurking behind a corner for the sake of a rapidly changed and re-emoted moment.

"The pretense being…"

"Abs, no pretense."

"That I'm implying to you that any day misused is a *question mark*, a *dash*, a…

"Sarah."

Her thoughts came out fluidly, like she had been trying to match words to feelings since our conversation days before. She had thought and re-considered. And though her declaration that she hadn't been thinking, that she'd been *chilling*, appeared to be discounted by her current focus – that eternal paradox: that which is not thought (at least basically thought) can't be said – I felt a panging sensitivity. The guilt of being offered her strong care for flailing me.

72

But unlike previous turns the sensation didn't just blossom into shame or shielding or inner-keening– of looking at nowhere but the ground - but also into a feeling more joyously summative, of thanks.

It was becoming clear to me that Goodman would not talk more about his medical predisposition than was visible through air, sound and sight.

Whatever it was, it still lacked a basic means of manifestation, a presentation mechanism. And so in lieu of it I began to adopt what I perceived to be his own pacific demeanor, thereby answering my own question as to what I should be doing.

Not that I didn't have questions, one of which sat with me in particular, less a new and revelatory piece of information than something I had been reminded of, that I recalled being told when I was younger.

"Are you a descendent of FDR?"

His head straightened. "Not a descendent." There was something unmistakable in his voice, the color of which I first thought sounded nearest to guilt or embarrassment.

Perhaps the guilt, I continued to think, of an uncontrollable blood relation being a ballad, an event, a glorification, a defining characteristic.

Really quickly Tony, as I see my piece – as it reads – briefly summons the topic on its own accord (and why not, I guess? It is the truth): Yes, I share blood with Franklin Roosevelt. My family originally came from Fairhaven, Massachusetts, then from Chicago, then from Cold Spring. In the first and last of those places they came to know another family, also mercantile transients. Enough so for the families to con-vene families and to share roots within a large tree of inheritance which for my parents resulted in a bare-boned, exogenously dictated letter of congratulations regarding my birth from the then-ailing president just months before his end.

Vera was forming and stockpiling a thought before realizing that I had another sentence in me.

"I mean, the twentieth century was spent developing a puristic, over-saddled fear of inflation."

"Thanks to us," she responds. Humble deflating laughter.

"Thanks to you guys," I say, my pointer finger a faux-admonishing horizontal at Weimar's dire example. She laughs again.

"But it was a convergence too," she continues.

"A realization," I add on collaboratively, "that an obvious culprit would effectively instill a basic, ministerial fear of inflation."

"Which explains much of Volcker-Greenspan."

"Yes!" I am right there. "Capital."

"Wealth."

"A participant's fear of diminishment."

To which Lydia half-raises her hand before preemptively putting it down and Tony turns to a page in the large text before him, rabbit-eared with annotation. Vera's glass-clad eyes remained fixed on me, like she was ready for a continuation in agreement, or, if proven necessary, an argument. Her phone etched a firm rectangle in her brown paper bag-colored pants that drooped above fluttering calves, black clogs.

G oodman refocused his attention toward the orchestra, the vocal pastiche: out-party provocations met with calm, anticipatory affirmation, performed as if they were lines read, the stress of their memorial imprint, to his ears, borrowed and noticeable as the Long Island Sound.

Eventually he fared back to the drips of his memory. He recalled, ideated, his legs knocking and rolling over the rosewood prie-dieu, his body, along with all the other blue-topped bodies, politely and squarely keeled toward the chancel where a rectangular-faced older student spoke purposely, with prudence and cringe pizzazz.

He thought about *that* night, to when they parted from the yellow light and sharp handsome faces of the ballroom, finding themselves on the double-lined yellow, quiet, muted, municipal, paint-shaven, of residential New Haven. They walked over road's center, hips shuffling from parallel to contiguous, the night windless.

Or the night he had invited her down from Northampton - Dad reckoned that Meg and Al Channing would be okay with it - calling her from a hallway phone at Saybrook College as he eradicated or sought to eradicate all softness in his voice, prompting a kind, laughing *Who is this?* from the other side of the call. He asked her about the second weekend in October.

She responded by getting on a bus at Springfield weeks later, her autumn-cool coffee still in her hand as she exited at

Grove Street on an early Saturday afternoon to the sight of Moira and Ham's lone boy, his hands plopped in his black jean pockets, confident, imperfect, his white shirt starched gray, his calves propelling toward the leather bag Jamie Channing had hauled from the trunk to the ground which he now lifted in the direction of his car.

"Standing challenge!" a student proclaimed across the procession, his feet following his words into a flexed, bent pose, contending with the slender-faced student at the chancel who bested him in height, disposition (very much the performative disposition of an older child, a late Joe Kennedy) and tolerability, if not intelligence.

A quiet Saturday afternoon. Spouses addressed spouses and siblings siblings on front lawns. The car drove on through its passengers' reintroduction and well-wishing, the connection, for now, still primarily a familial one.

"Standing challenge!" repeated the student, severe eyes under thick black brows.

A night when the sharp defined corners of politeness and cocktail party goodness ("How's your mother!" "No! How's *your* mother?") were replaced with a less conjured substitute. Not the total eradication of artifice but a half-knowing exercise of it.

"The war's *over*, Carney. It has been for almost two decades."

What made him move now, present as he should've been at the Buckley Political Union? Something impassioning and misguiding, something deeply vague, from which Goodman considered, like a man considering a fragment or a bad un-destined idea, the difference between vagueness inherent and vagueness in lieu of definition, in lieu of the explicative. Between things unanswerable and those that require time, space, energy, love.

But when he tried to find the poem within the novel – those verbal sapphires and emeralds that would lift him from his restlessness, his nonenumerations – all he got were more moving images, dispatches from that night, the farrago of his brain lacking the grounding of day.

"Private?" said the senior, his voice far handsomer than his face. "Did *private* save the economy back in '29? In '31?"

He was back over the traffic lines, the early morning now completely staid, motionless, guided by nothing but the light of the front porch that illuminated his incoming date, passing into her place of temporary residence, the door its own soft planetary shade. His arms were condensed into his chest, his face lulling as he waited for the door to close and the figure just departed to reappear, through one of the six windows – long rows, short columns – on the house's jeweled face.

But there was always that initial realization you had in your first or second year, where you looked over at your neighbor's desk and saw a superlative mark. And you thought: I don't know what this person's voice sounds like. But they look at their grade, stoically expectant, put it in their leather briefcase, look up at you, smile – one could interpret this smile as contrived, but I never did; more of an effort for explanation, a descendent protecting an inheritance, a way of being – rise from their seat, reach for their bag of newfound treasures and leave you there to think about your lesser composition, about role, about place.

Following him around campus was the act of following a gazing, knowing head which blinked prior to refocusing on a steel-glass addition, or a recently patented letterhead, or renovations to the green-shuttered windows of Redlich Hall, his feet syncopating with the curved calibrated pathways, with the hallways through the main building, through an archway, a perfect angle on one side and artfully distended on the other, to the sitting bulls, to the woods, and, finally, to Lake Wononscopomuc, where for reasons undisclosed (and yet reasons I somehow understood) he was most insistent on stopping.

On our way back up to the school we passed by a sylvan overhang, whose lushness he gazed at long and specifically enough to suggest a personal connection with the arbor – like it justified the Hotchkiss School's warm, privileged unreality.

He walked slowly to the hill's peak before asking for my phone so he could take two pictures, one of the posterior lake and one of the dispersed buildings of bright brick, wind-scraped. The only modicum of ownership he could fathom affording on these treaded, accruing grounds.

The halls and dorms formed one long east-west rectangle inter-broken with pathways, culminating on the campus' east end with a dome and on its west end with a building more inspired, a square glass face overlooking an Edo Garden and cacti and vestiges of chaparral and saucer-shaped metallic chairs with plastic seats that baked in the higher vantages of sun. The two structures stared at each other stone-eyed from hundreds of yards, one a figment of one time, the other a changed, more chaotic, more conscious one, and in the space between them there existed a rhapsody of administration buildings, institutes, recreation centers, classrooms and six dorms - three facing three – and beneath them the many lifeforms of the Pomona Valley, historic and current, natural and formulated: yuccas and kalanchoes and foxtail and feathergrass that were replaced down-campus by lawns, by the dream of Lakewood and Thousand Oaks and Irvine. A dream watered into the night by streams of life, by the resource that had been taken from the less parched and photically plentiful parts of the continental terra and dragged, like its diasporic inhabitants, toward the lower westward part of the continent.

She ran down the concrete-filled stairs two at a time, consulting superficially the railing's thickly painted steel.

Upon hearing my name, I cumbersomely lifted my eyes from the lawn, removed my headphones and angled my feet and eyes toward the bottom of the stairs, from which a pathway led to a series of larger pathways down which students traveled from glass to dome to dorm on long boards, in tank tops, in flat-brimmed hats, in board shorts. My eyes opened as they rose. I didn't know her, or her name. But I did recognize her. I echoed back in confirmation.

She explained her reasons for haste, for approaching me, her body a fitful response to the temperate February cool: jeans, Blundstones, striped thermal, Nano vest.

Something about… which of my articles was it? She thought in place. Was it Joyce and *foot and mouth disease*? Austen's masterful marriage of the verbally scientific and artistic?

Or was it the unexpected diversity and virtuosity of mid to late millennial Tumblr poetry? Or college and careerism? Or career versus vocation?

She couldn't remember where one wall stopped and the other began but exhibited disparate knowledge of the building, my building, and its many rooms both square and less square, looking at me around and over her big comfort-mood glasses. So much so that she did what all in the cloud generation are at least accustomed to doing: she vagued and tripped her own voice, pretending to know less about me than perhaps she did. Where I was from (I was from New York, which I had a feeling she knew, though I couldn't prove it). What I studied (I made it very clear in *college and careerism* that I had done the DC internship program). Normal courses of information-gathering felt, in the information age, unnatural, like wearing a cravat, like cheating.

She talked circles around me. She beat me to constellations of fact and insight. She beat me to jokes. And as she did so as I stood there with a dumb red gleeful face and small focused eyes, regurgitating *supers* and *dopes* and *for sures*. I was mesmerized, half-embarrassed, trying to spleen gregariousness from my big chest. I asked for her name – an easy, significant question to ask – to which she replied it was Sarah Abbott.

We finished our guacamole, our tacos and our Modelos at a European's pace (less determined, less insistent as to whether the future is the place to reside). When the time came I lightly asked for the check and when it arrived she inquired un-laboriously, her hand parsing the caverns of her lap-perched purse, about the check's median. We placed two aqua cards down which the waiter came to fetch before coming back with new paper but the same polyvinyl. We signed – just one line, unlike the American two lines – and rose above the last of our plates and the gold-foiled bottles and ascended the spiral staircase up to the ground floor and out into the world, past Archbishop's and up Carlisle Lane to the main road, where we forked. We exchanged cheeks, allowed for one or two more exchanges, including possible forthcoming arrangements. Phone in hand, she smiled the radiance one bequeaths to a passing crush (one that enters into the radar of preference and fitness at a wrong or busy or not especially impassioned time) before our shoulders started ducking backwards and we vanished into the night in separate directions, her to the tube and I street-bound, round a rotary traffic-wise and onward, toward Westminster Bridge.

Shera,

I just had a burrito at the place we used to go on The Periphery. What a strange neighborhood: the stately brick mediocrity of the prewar 90s blends with the 100s, the only thing distinguishing the even-edged units being the assets and inheritances inside, the ones in the 90s always having a pathway unseen, the nugatory walls between the kitchen and living room busted out so that light can hit suede, marble, oak.

But, as always, the one tell (unless the neighborhood has a private garage): cars. The 90s cars all imports: Mercedes' and Japanese SUVs for wealth more pronounced and Subarus and Volvos for the more conscious.

And the burritos! Once four dollars, now Hamiltons. The store once Timberlands, now Doc Martens. Though I'm not sure how familiar you are with the new clientele since you moved to Westchester. You were still in Woodside back when we used to go regularly, back before you met Priya. Out of car-driving but not yet to machine learning. Far from Queens but far from your reverse commute to Armonk.

How are you? I saw a picture of Churchill and Nehru in top hats recently – Churchill in an Abe Lincoln, Nehru in more of a, let's say, Homburg. Churchill looked, as he often did, ridiculous, a coincidental politician, whereas Nehru looked smart and handsome, of a stern, determined humor. I'm not sure where I saw it – I must've been on a curiosity quest, trying to re-claim and repaint fading shards of memory on the Internet. But I can only hope it summoned the bulldog's elegance in the stead of his brutality. He must've known that Nehru was just as good as him, better than him.

It made me think of our inception. Many things do. It can never not make me laugh: a tenured teacher grading an untenured's class and not being able to keep quiet. I had never had a serious science education, and so I couldn't help but pontificate during that run-up to the yeast respiration lab, my bid to learn mixed with my far-too-confident presumption that – almost Darwin-like - it was all intuitive and analogical, able to fasten itself onto existing architecture after moments or minutes of application. I think you felt for (perhaps even identified with) my innocence. You saw a proud chest. You saw a voice unafraid – too unafraid – to pan from door to window. And you saw incorrectness. So you corrected me. The kids laughed, and I could feel the expansion of your smile, your slight hemming frustration, and I laughed and practically forgot why I was there. Well! *I submitted,* Then I'll stop mutilating the signs, *allowing as I did the class to proceed with the pre-trial diagnostics. I followed along well enough with the stoichiometry. But the letters and names that I had tried to narrate and make characters out of remained foreign.*

You apologized to me after class, lamented that your finite knowledge didn't allow you to crack open certain scientific chambers – these were profound questions of chemistry available to only a few – and I told you that I had given you an across the board ten.

She lived a long northeastward walk from Grand Central, a summer or winter cab ride (extraneous to public transport because of its diagonality) but optimal for the first winds of September. It was dark. Tim and Joe walked with the purpose of slacks and blazers but with the boyishness and oblivion of still-teens, their heads perched vertically. Doglike, they responded to sounds and sensations that seemed to come both unexpectedly and predictably, from around corners as well as continually and non-abruptly across the island's axes: car horns, tires rolling and braking, bikes clicking, voices rising and quelling in bisecting conversation, in stationary al fresco dining, in the cordiality and distance of occasionally congregating friends, in the tailored but sometimes loosening chatter of colleagues, in the loving admonishment of parents.

Goodman loved the untangling creation, the procession of moment unpredicted to the next, kinetic, trivially anxious...

Unlike, he thought, the weightier and more decided anxiety of destination, of end shape. The roots of this anxiety he contained – indeed, it was bourgeoning - but toward it he refused to front a solitary unchanging stance. His brain deemed unwelcome the idea of categorical rebellion. No, radicalism lay in footnoting, in conditional agreement and dissent, in the pronunciation of each and every paragraph, each and every pivot. Some of this anxiety was inhibiting, some frustrating, some workable, some humanizing.

He didn't, for instance, know how to feel about the prospect of not being able to control the person he was to become, the widespread (and, tautologically, not wrong) idea that sex, education and family make the woman or man. Not that they weren't parts of him he didn't accept – that he most certainly couldn't control – just that he wanted some control over that which shaped and clothed and supported the half-destined foundation.

They rang politely onto a black key backdropped by a wall of translucent varicolored marble, black and green and orchid. The door opened. They took the elevator to floor five. They knocked.

There, in her entryway, in the windowed backdrop the 59th Street Bridge – a procession of moving orange pillared by static white – she stood. She held in her hands a votive-shaped glass, stationary just below wrists of rising and sliding bangle, of metal, gold, colored bead.

Her hair: still purple.

"How wonderful we could negotiate this," she murmured, with a quiet extroversion.

It had been a far too ordinary expectation, the idea – every last unspoken step – of Tim moving to New Haven, of donning a suit for understood reasons (or perhaps it was for no reason at all), of boarding a train, possibly with a friend, of watching Norwalk and Greenwich and Pelham pass by, of crossing the river and down the Harlem plateau, of entering the hollowed tunnel, of exiting into marble and arch and emerald and celestial tapestry, of orienting - pant hem twisting, tie hanging - toward car or foot, of ringing on the apartment owned by the fading heirloom.

She sat them down on colored felt, directed them to rotting textured cheeses, toward cheese solvents - rice crackers, French bread, cashews - toward jam and fig. She picked herself up muscle, bone, and cloth and walked through a doorway and came back with two glasses, tinged brown at their base. The liquid dove and circled as she handed the concoctions to them.

She asked about Mom. Tim told her that Mom had been going to see Mom and Dad (*her* Mom and Dad, as his audience understood. It was most polite to refer to your subject as if you were inhabiting them) in Washington every two or so months. She had even thought about moving down there so that she could look after Dad.

Laura cooed intrigue over the glass table as raucous breaths rolled and warbled from Tim's right, through a field of fig and cashew Joe happily interchanged.

And how was *she* dealing with that predicament of generation and family?

"As knowers of Moira would expect," Tim responded. "With the same expression she's had on her face for decades."

Tim barely knew his host but had always perceived her – through vague childhood encounters and, mostly, tall-telling – to be quite willing to talk. Ever since *he* had died that's all there was to do. And what information she possessed. She was the one who had been at Warm Springs at heart's slowing, an intermediary, a translator, a dual sympathizer, an ally in a time of familial strife and worldly uncertainty.

Now she was here, dispensing alcohol to a *tabula rasa*, an unremembering infant at the time of that death, wholly nonexistent during his sixty-three years of life. Her loose silk clothes existed about her, dignified, certain, cooperative. Her Irish Setter noodled eel-like at the backs of her ankles, its golden body half-covered by couch, its proud neck supporting a gulping uncertain face and squatting jaw, its brown eyes dreaming of Rhinebeck.

When the word president finally did come up – not even President Roosevelt, but *president, presidency* – Tim, his eyes glassing over, his heart consuming the ephemeral joy of drink, conjured a cocktail-hourly question.

"What did *you* call him?" he asked. Her contemporary, her blood, her relational subject, her public servant.

Tinctures of scintillation. No elicitations of fatigue. No eye-roll. Not even a trace of overacting (perhaps she *was* that good).

She dropped her palm to the long neck beneath her and fished up loose soft gold flesh.

"I can't speak for everyone else but I used to call him '*dahling*.'"

They walked up Sutton to York and cut across four long blocks in the 60s toward Joe's childhood apartment. They were smoking. They were drunk, having been fed agglomerates of cheer and repartee before being dumped into the streets, told to go find fun, affiliation. Shafts of spired rectangular art deco to their southwest, lit under the opacity of the urban sky, the smaller delicate Chrysler succeeded by the larger more brutal Empire State.

To their north, cars crept onto the bridge only to become icons visible from Laura's apartment.

They kept walking north, under the abutment's long cavern, under the final girder.

Replaced, on the other side of 60th, by an emergent sound. Rubber, air, impact, lightly clanking iron. The sound of soft passage.

Tim looked to his left – a park. Past the wire diamonds separating the park from the street he saw nothing but dark court.

Then, just barely, he saw a shoe departing from concrete, lightly, lowly but for what seemed like moments as the shoe disappeared again in dark static before reappearing in shadowed motion toward the ground, allowing Tim to parse through the façade of dim colorless gray. The ball made an angled jut with the concrete and passed from right down under the popliteal and up to the dribbler's left hip, faring out of sight before coming back into concert with his left hand. He turned. Goodman could now see his full height. Huge. 6'6" maybe: beard, rounded shoulders, spindly chest-to-foot, motionarily eaglelike. He sunk and rose, his arms flowing in mnemonic wave toward body – the ball's majority risen above his eyes – then outward toward the basket, like they were boneless, like they were mills of energy and rotation and momentum, the ball sailing clockwise toward the lone ring of metal and acrylic, expedient but patient, its deliverer now fully grounded.

1969

A Dispatch on Goodness *(from those who might seek to undercut it!)*
The Apollonian: the construction of a world to toe into line that which you care about: aesthetic, morality, authorship. Rules.

Here's one rule: never spend more time talking about yourself than you do asking someone about themselves (of course, someone always loses). The rule of the cocktail party. And don't just feign listening either. Teach those northward muscles to love *asking questions, to* love *empathizing, to love conjuring answers to honest dilemmas. To love - when your number is called – compiling anecdotal comparatives, kinship via theme, arc, plot point.*

Here's another: be a benefactor. I know how this sounds. There are barriers to that game - namely, that the ability to give must be met by the pretense of a literal have. *Not true. Benefactorship is a vantage from which you journal someone, from which you marvel in the constellation of character points (quiet but funny, gregarious but pained, creative but grounded), from which you pat input without being too intense, too drawn out. From which you compliment, show love.*

Here's another: Read. Not that goodness and reading can't be separate - plenty of read tyrants and un-read Samaritans. But goodness *goes back to how you draw yourself in the lives of others. And that outline is edged with the sheerness of magnanimity just as it is with the sinuosity of knowledge and inference.*

91

Another: be collaborative. Center on the places where you and the talker agree. It is a wonderful exercise in empathy (But, I warn you, it might also prevent you from ever making a stand on anything).

Another: verse yourself in voice. Indoor v. outdoor. Public v. private. It will serve as a marvelous tool for learning and measuring social topographies (At least until your internal registers, sick of the orchestration, sick of the effort, *rebel against you).*

Another: refinement is goodness' cousin, is a marker – even if salved with artifice – of sincerity. It will clarify your efforts, your angelism, even as the world's boorishness passes you by, saps you of your ability to explain.

Another: Try not to lose your ability to explain.

Another: Your explanatory capacities tucked safely under, try not to look out the window and gasp.

1964

The Oeuvre (Or, the way it was before the way it is)

Last month, Attorney General Robert Kennedy, upright and in grasp of his kind smile - his Falstaff - met with the writer James Baldwin, Clarence B. Jones, advisor to Martin Luther King, and a number of other black leaders at a big apartment in Columbus Circle.

The legend goes thusly: Mutual admirations. An agreement on productivity. Then: Jerome Smith's tears. Then: Kennedy's rally to service. Then: Smith's Joycean moment ("I will never never – never - join the military"). Then: Lorraine Hansberry's balk at, indirectly, whether the state of race relations was really on the verge of such a discursive breakthrough. "If you can't understand what this young man is saying, then we are without any hope at all, because you and your brother are representatives of the momentary best that a White America can offer."

Hansberry turned back to Smith: He's the one of us to whom you should listen. Power not in the extraordinary but the common, not in the ought but the is.

"They seemed possessed," Kennedy later said, who nonetheless moved on to years of timely compassion after the meeting, in the years preceding his un-timely death. During the meeting he had apparently elected to seek out the less "hysterical" members of the room; the ones, to translate Kennedy, who could hide their sorrows *under an epidermis of education and trauma, who sought to make the crucial step of parting the side of their fellow wayward Israelites with whom they shared skin and journey. From John Casor to Jefferson, from Adams and Madison to Eli Whitney to Dred Scott to emancipation to sharecropping to segregation to Madison Grant and Lothrop Stoddard to* Brown.

After the meeting, Kennedy ordered J. Edgar Hoover to tap the phone of Jones.

Weeks after the meeting, he phoned into Alabama, where Vivian Jones, escorted by the national guard, by federal dictate, proceeded past George Wallace and into Foster Auditorium to complete her registration at the University of Alabama.

A year after passing under the lights of the 59ᵗʰ Street Bridge Goodman was in his car, briskly soaring up Eisenhower's Route 91, a north-south radius across non-Maine New England's rectangle.

Halfway up Massachusetts he veered off the highway and crossed the Connecticut River into Northampton, past barbers, bars (sprawling like they do in still-operative factory towns), convenience stores, small markets, diners, hardware stores, mechanics, a movie theater, a public performance center, past a high-turreted church, past Smith College's quadrangle, where he looked out at students walking across grass and pathway to get to class. It was midweek. He wondered if he'd see her, after months of failed deliberation and quietness, of circuitous navigation.

It had been a spring of copious performing, of Thornton Wilder and Bertolt Brecht (the former of which Jamie had come down to see), of not attending class, of a letter to home from Yale about Tim's truancy, of a call from home to DC, and, finally, of a strained steaming summer in DC, where he politely lived with his loyal judgmental grandmother and renally cursed grandfather on Kalorama Road while he tried to piece together rigorous knowledge and barely nascent experience into additional experiences, into a career. He had at one point the privilege of interviewing for five minutes with Ben Bradlee – him and Mom had once dated – but, uncommon for other 19-year-olds but repetitiously so for Tim, he shot too high, insisting, rather than accepting duties couriel or clerical or administrative, that he aspired to cover civil rights. He was willing to bus down, camp out, be paid at first by story, learn sourcing and information-gathering from a more seasoned hand.

Bradlee, his legs perched near the height of his head, his breaths tucked over and under his slang-modified Brahmin staccato, the whole of his body an obtuse V, could do nothing but smile at this regional-familial acquaintance. He gave him the cultural special. Not a yes or a no but a re-asking. *Civil rights, eh?* Then he relieved him, graciously, beneficently. In a way he'd be entertained enough to tell his mom about.

The chance to cover civil rights at the *Post* never did work out, but Bradlee did help him get a job at *Newsweek*. Which didn't keep the letter that was on its way from Cambridge that summer from arriving on Kalorama. It was very caring, very unthreatening. The main concern, it stated – explicit and Unitarian, much like Mom and Dad's non-resurrection-believing churchgoers – were not his grades. It was the incompletes; the essays that were never filed while learning the cadences, the *verfremdungseffekt*, of *Mother Courage and Her Children*; while lobbying the city of New Haven to mint a municipal Civil Rights committee; while calling Jamie incessantly.

Now, his grades – his lack of grades – were being dictated to him down the North Atlantic coast, through the brevity of deliberated words and solitarily made points, the voice of his mother and even less fussy, quiet, bearded, bookish father forming together, disparately, coherently. What would change? Would he now go back to school and complete, rather than not complete, classes?

He felt none of those traditional signs of urgency. No remorse, no worry, no manifestation of any latent, deferred stress. But also: no resentment, no will to prove. He was just *here*, couched into keratin. A glass cube in the desert.

Past the college he found his way into a non-columnar red brick house of worship, which hoisted a short, round, bell-less steeple. He made his way through the front doors and a residential-looking vestibule and into a modest nave of just seven bisected rows, all white, perfectly linear. It reminded him of First Parish in Cambridge. Everything lay on a step-high plateau, the tabernacle emphasized by a *lack* of altar, where an old spruce piano squatted between two square-potted lilies, the wall in back sculpted and carved with what resembled the lively core geometry of a Tibetan door. The windows were ancillary, unstained, oval-topped.

The Unitarians: deeply respectful. Disinterested in attitudinal radicalism.

And yet: radically unspiritual.

Or rather: believers in spirit as beauty unfound and designed to be unfound. In spirit as mystery. The mystery of the historically and empirically remote, in the legacy of those properties being made less remote, willed into awesome being by generational heritage, by the power of human aspiration, by voice and hand echoing through a warbling, refracted medium. The mystery of *Mood Indigo*, of key on wood, pin and string. The mystery of voice in tune, what it elicits about capacity, limit (the drama, the *tell*, of almost hitting your note but just missing), subjectivity, love. The mystery of mixing light and water, of air, thought.

He sat in the nave looking up at the modest immaterial ceiling, characteristically doubtful. He tried to approximate himself while losing track of what such an exercise entailed, what it signified, the core of his stomach pushing into his leather jacket's blank space like air into an empty church.

Wind warbling over the soft, clean ground and its autumnal fodder, lifting and repositioning around the green-caked brick, under the glassy sky, angling toward the lowering distancing pivot of the pending solstice like beauty partitioned from beholder, like energy from source.

Wind flowing through bodies, tightening lips, numbing noses, dispersing the ends of hat-clad strains of hair, lightly obstructing woolen arm flows, the bodies shuffling but bracing, enjoying, disappearing under columns of red and white, through doorways, into rooms through which the eye allowed just enough wherewithal to see vague scarved shapes, notating or book mining or bored and desk-askew.

He had given Jamie no frontward notice that he would be coming, deciding that if he intercepted her right where the quadrangle met Elm then it was by design. He didn't necessarily believe that last part, but even if he didn't, he did believe that some things just happened and others don't and an encounter would either be the first or the last. He hadn't seen her since early fall - after she had trained down the eastern seaboard to come see him in the heat of the mid-Atlantic summer; after she had visited New Haven, a semester of further, and heightened, absenteeism. But this time his misplaced energies did not compromisingly wander about to on-site activities, to plays, to dress rehearsals of political theater, to advocacy. Now – and to his fear – they were projectiling more speculatively, more distantly, more internally.

It was the reason he hadn't talked to her in two weeks; he hadn't talked to *anyone* in two weeks. And now – well, it was nothing destructive, he returned to with casualness and typical confidence. Though he knew that such wayward wonderment wasn't productive. He was a Goodman, the child of two parents who had dedicated their life to pedagogy – Mom to school-founding and administering and Dad to instructing. He was the first son, the only boy, astray from school and pathway toward nothing more formed than the small, confined shapes of the many nondescript Smith College classrooms surrounding him.

Forty-five minutes at the Quadrangle's juncture with Elm and he saw no more than twenty people. The day was now tending toward darkness. No sign of Jamie's tall waist and golden hair and slow, inward-footed movement. No. Her socks were departed from shoe in a flu-lit room somewhere. Chance was now conceived history.

A week later he had sifted through valuables versus disposables and cleaned out his room and left his books on two balanced but uneven stacks at the outset of his residential hallway and packed his car and, by 10am, had crossed the Tappan Zee Bridge. By noon, the Delaware Water Gap. By night he had made it to the Berney's in Squirrel Hill, whom he had called from State College and who fed him a late dinner and boarded him in their guest room, where he slept, loomed over by a Carnegie Tech pennant and a Mazeroski luckily and gleefully rounding third. When he awoke, he crossed the border into Ohio, into Indiana, through Gary.

Disparities in heat, humidity, color, elevation, terrain. Green to swamp to lake to city to slowly caving lumber to yellowing plain to star to mountain to every kind of rock – tan, black lava, red – to sand to sun to moon to mist to rain to green.

And *us*, fluid and aspirational, poised for indecision (for somberness, insanity) as much as the land: inhabiting, migrating, forcefully taking, hating, misunderstanding, fearfully coexisting, syncing. The general policy being to stay epidermal. To affirm property. To say *sorry* at moments of physical obstruction. To exchange xenophilic intent. An eaten taco or burger or slice or noodle. A shared sport.

And under shared comforts, under the evening lull of bodies walking through food and department stores, under eager feet tucked beneath the legibility, the uniformity, of boots and sneakers and slippers and heels: dreams. Strange dreams. Ones that seize the many properties of kitsch (evervisible, media-strewn) and texture them with specificity of place, time, association. Dreams of predictability - of assuming the un-extraordinary mantles of love and work. Dreams of disavowal. Dreams of uncertainty. Dreams of departure. Dreams of return.

He reached Denver and decided to parallel rather than broach the mountains. He fled south, toward Colorado Springs and then on down the plain past Pueblo and, once he crossed the border, streamed off the highway westward, marking the resurgence of elevation. He faintly deciphered Spanish road signs and mercantile summonses: Angel Fire, Valle Escondido, Taos, Arroyo Seco and, finally, the Rio Grande Valley's front step. He got out of his car and walked and, where pathway stopped, saw, peering down into the malpaís, the corrugations made of disparate-colored sediments which marked erosion's long progression (where it was master, where it was merely influential). At the bottom of the steep canyon went the river. And it went. But it went as does a person walking to work: with feet of width. Just present enough so that when all movements have ceased – vehicles, bodies, minds - you hear the sound of the water's persistence on the yet uncut earth. The sound of contestation. Like the water is more concerned with traveling than how it does so – with merely getting to the Gulf.

David,

I'm not sure how often you check this account, but I wanted to let you know how I got it. It was right after I saw you at the Home Depot, and I was driving home down Route 20, and I had what was formerly the dread of the phonebook; that the only public recognition of your personhood was a goddamn number. At which point I'd have to call that number and hoist upon it the many questions I have for you - your livelihood, your family, your current spiritual locale - which is burdensome for you and uncomfortable for me. But when I got to my door it immediately occurred to me – it rarely does – to walk down into my basement and fire up the clunky aqua-hipped iMac. I watched as it filled up my dusty workspace – where I work, fail and occasionally succeed with wood and metal - with strange compatible light. I clicked on the hardware that I had once passionlessly set up. I inputted the meager Wi-Fi. The first entrance was you, in what occurred to me was Cummington or one of those eastern Berkshire towns, standing in front of your branded truck. I looked through the About, the Services, the Testimonials. I found your Facebook (I don't have a Facebook, so I'm not sure how they let me see this), which had your wife, your dog, your little boy. The first picture was of you and him, eyes pointed at the other. He was old enough to resemble you – same small eyes - and the next of him in the curled lap of Mom at Wahconah Park. And the next of you and the dog at Bish Bash Falls...

Dear David,

I think the idea that he represents anything but a venality that shores up after 30 seconds of being introduced – that he embodies deliberation or an idea – is insane. Enjoy what he represents for you: a lambasting of yesterday's holes, the drunkening of a jobless technoglobe, the singing of a song of impossibility (or insincerity) - anti-corruption, unmitigated liberty, innocent return. But please, don't give a line ten sides.

It starts at the crown, pares back after decades (few for some, for others, many). To where it flourishes in the meantime, a point of scientific dependency: for biology, a contention of capability; for people, a contention of exhibition and *degree* of exhibition. The acceptability of boyish flow, even a scrag of days-old hair, reflective of nothing but prolonged intention, a chore delayed. But then, a week. Three months. Six months. The hair flanks, adds, bushes, drops. The neck gruffs, thickens. The jaw vagues.

And the brain – that it is non-verbal is key – takes authorship. This is the point of conflict. Pileous happenstance becomes self-insistence, alt-expression. Shape's edges get questioned, and facial contour: that's only where it starts. Clothes bag, widen, cut, trim, fit, brighten, blacken. Words lose syllables, are slurred, bent, spiraled. Journey's curve is more persistently round, oblong. Surfaces, the ones in which we operate upon, are run with mercury.

He worked in the Taos ski valley in the winter of 1963, convinced every morning that today, the 1957 Ford Del Rio stirring itself awake in the icy sun of Arroyo Seco, would be the day the car did not make it up the mountain.

Upon arriving at the mountain, he would see Snakedance's blunt impossibility, its point of inception rising into cloud and chill and then dropping, turn-less, as goers meandered in inch-long syllables down the strait. All day he would look at the straightaway (it *was* the mountain) as Goodman, clad in layers from his old life that, in the chill of the valley, were singly inadequate – long john shielded by denim topped by cotton, canvas, fleece, flannel – alternated between the hot drink stand and the two innovations that had transformed the resort, one a three-sided bar and the other a cable rope, both of which carried legs lagged by the weight and length of skis up the hill, transforming the hill into a commodity of repetitious extremity and recreation.

The only hindrance was the course's stark reality. More likely the attendants were those with a certain healthy but fractious relationship with planned living. These people were geographically disparate. There was a man Goodman recalled named Earl Leftwich who would wake up on Saturdays in Amarillo when it was still dark, drive his Jeep flush across the eastern New Mexican plane, be back in his car at three and back home by eight. His dance was especially cavalier and perilous – he almost looked to be going back *up* the mountain when he pivoted, stepping when he should have been sliding - but once he made it down the pass his face, uncovered by tartan, smiled through a tangy Scot's Irish red. He never shed the smile; in the four months Goodman watched Earn Leftwich he never saw him fall.

Bill,

It was wonderful getting to see you in the Back Bay again. I'm happy you're finally retired. I never knew you then but know from legend the kinds of days you worked. I hope it prompts you to see more movie matinees, take more walks with the shelties round the Common, get involved *(one of the great umbrella-signifying inventions of the leisure class), not miss church on Sundays, go places – your sister in Sarasota, your daughter in Denver – see former colleagues, drink at noon, drink coffee in the PM, read articles on your phone.*

I hope you come out to New Lebanon. We can relitigate our first encounter: the great Brattle Street Battle of Boxing Day 2013, when you unveiled, in no particular order, the fateful L and CL words. I'm not sure which one caught me more on one heel: I hate the substance of the word Libertarian *– sure, why don't we take what's an enriching and generally wide-ranging idea and make it the Lord God – but the way you said* classically liberal. Classically! *I would've happily probed you more litigiously had we been in another place or wrinkle – you were, after all, Bill Benson, formerly Suffolk County, Benson Quinn (how you* never ran for Congress!*) – but we were amid politeness, surrounded by festive ham and Grey Poupon and dates wrapped in bacon. We were comfortable and happy and had implacable smiles on our face.*

And there was another thing: that despite your tieless suit, your slipper-fetishizing dress shoes, your faded and slicked back head of

*hair, despite the many things you undoubtedly thought too about me
— an odd way for God to channel and dispense of creative-intellectual
talent, giving it to a man of such shape and temperament and
impulse; how reassuring it would be if he turned out to care about*
anything — *I really liked you. I saw how your mouth moved, the way
your arms unintentionally draped and swung faster than your body.
I saw someone fearing, knowing, caring. Who knew his certainty
carried him merely to the party's onset.*

The museum's entrance sign was red with white letters - straight, like the font of a long-standing bank or life insurer, the *The* smaller than *Norman*, *Rockwell* and *Museum*. The building was a similar barn red, with a modern window at its rear, segmented into five parts that bayed out onto a large northward Berkshire view.

Inside, the central room watered into side and backrooms, full of snaking white benches that brought you a whole foot closer toward the image upon which you peered, barrel-shaped ceilings and, on the walls themselves, the content. The powerful prosaic inheritance bequeathed by the creator. *The Problem We All Live With* was there, Ruby Bridges in her little white dress and shoes, book cradled, vying for the life of education, of basic citizenhood. So was *Graduate*. So was *Freedom from Want*, the aproned matriarch and the elevated turkey. So were a couple of pieces more interestingly lit and dreamily colored, like a Hopper. So were the various meditations – they felt, to me, like lamentations – on working goodness: a downward peering cop saddled with leather and a doting, stripe-shirted, denim-clad, foot-wagging child; the capped lineman in flannel at the top of a telephone poll; the man arisen in *Freedom of Speech*, his hands supplicant on the pew.

Amid the Friday afternoon crowd – which, algorithmically, landed three or more people at *The Problem We All Live With* and *Freedom of Speech* at any time, the rush of retirees and half-day workers from Manhattan, Brooklyn, Cambridge, Boston – I had lost Goodman. His suspenders and fleece were nowhere. Somewhere, but not here. I checked the bathroom. The car. I came back into the central room when I realized there was one room to my right I had not yet checked, where, once I proceeded through its cased opening, I found him sitting between the artworks, his cane splayed parallel to his thigh, his back, unlike when he walked, deadly straight.

He was one of two people in the room, the other a white-haired woman in cotton and corduroy. They looked into the same corner, the woman hand-on-jawing the painting on one corner's side while Tim vaguely interacted with the other, upon which sat a painting of two men, one in buckled black shoes and a tunic, the other in leather, buckskin, garter. A hound behind him, a book splayed open on his lap, the pilgrim's face looked to be pivoting, motioning, suggestive of more than one idea or feeling or encapsulation, while the native looked back with sharp discerning eyes. He had a strand of parchment that sat in his half-fisted right hand, ready to share its content, the European ready to receive it. Each man's face looked to be at an intersection where concern meets something more interesting, not just its negation but its alloying. Where a stream – rather than, indelibly, headed toward Elevation Zero – might just swell out across the hillside.

I rushed up the stairs, parted phone from mesh, loosely tied it to a white cord to salvage its reddening battery, rolled over onto my stomach and entered Safari, where I input what I could remember of the suffixed painting. Up it came: The Yale-ordained John Sergeant and Chief Konkapot. The apparent subject of a spiritual transition.

I read down: when Sergeant died of a cankerous fever in 1749, five years before the outbreak of the French and Indian

War, the Stockbridge Natives attended his funeral. One wrote on his tombstone *He's not within, false stone, there's not but Dust below*, which, happily, I pictured to be a friendly, democratic post-mortem dissension, a continuation of a conversation on transmogrified existence versus non-existence which the Natives, who welcomed Sergeant into their home and lives, perhaps took up in the quietness of word even in the wake of their supposed conversion. Disputes on fact, placid - even love-vying - rather than crises of sentiment.

To the Chronicle:

I write to you as a former employee who, when I first arrived in The Haight in the spring of '63, stayed in a room on Page Street right off a second story window on the building's baby blue facade. It cost 15 dollars a month. From the inside the place was madness – the cumulative material result of six waxing, turning, dizzying heads (half-including me, whose true tell was not the confusion and conglomeration of what he had, but what he had not). *But from the outside... To this day there is no city that so compares street by street, where the sun and development and odd beauty meet in such partnership (though admittedly I've never been to Cape Town, to Rio, to Medellin).*

It is why it is such a perfect culprit for what happened. A bunch of quirky scientists at Bell and Intel making chips and circuits and processors between the Bay and Basin, who at night talked through their beards and glasses about the revolution. *They were* sort've *like us (though none of us now admit it), with their pretense of extracurricularity, of idealism. I'm sure it's been hard enough for them to adjust, especially once the money men came in and sculpted the valley. The ones with firm names the likes of tree, water, rock, fruit, animal. The money pumpers, trying and trying more to turn their thought into ubiquity, a verb.*

But the money men did something that was also impressive – if unbearable. Institutionally of the east, *they heeded to the eccentricities and lack of eye contact of the men in beards and glasses. They hung up their coats, unmoored their ties, bought new wardrobes. All of which was designed to dissuade them from their shell of power, from intimidating: patterned running shoes, puffy jeans, tucked in tee shirts. A vain titanic marriage of capitalism and counterculture that fed off the banking industry's continual sadness and predictability – diminishing returns, bad practice, a lack of vernacular understanding, staid imagination – which peaked just about a decade ago, when the empires built by the ties started collapsing, when the world wanted nothing more than to marvel at boy geniuses drinking Stella in their boxers.*

Then two things happened (either of which were explainable): 1) the myths thoughtlessly created by the freshly turned thirty-somethings started cratering (and not just cratering, exploding*); and 2) this beautiful city, stuck as it is between the bay and ocean, became unlivable. The second story windows are now gazed through the by tees, jeans and sneakers.*

Goodman drove due west from Albuquerque, through Flagstaff, to Bakersfield. He found a place to stay in a town called Oildale and keyed into his smoky room and called his parents. He told his mom that he'd be in San Francisco tomorrow by midday, and she called up her brother.

The next day Tim arrived at the base of the staircase that led up to Uncle Elihu's house on Pacific Avenue, about fifty feet above the street. He walked up the stairs, knocked on the door. A Roosevelt-Wallace pin was tied into the screen door's vinyl.

Two weeks later he was reporting to work at *The Chronicle*'s gothic, white stucco locale at 901 Mission Street, the paper's inscription on both the Mission and 5th Street sides of the building. He was tasked at first with tracking, sourcing and correcting stories, but rarely, if ever, bylining them. This he was frustrated by. More than anything he wanted bylines. Bylines that were shaped and commodified by editors. Bylines that were determined by news and world, by moment. But still, bylines. He knew this to be, largely, a product of vanity. Still, he welcomed the urge, one he knew came from a will to sufficiency and, more ethereally, from an exploration of the variety and possibility of vocal avenue, of self-definition. He brought his urge to his uncle, a politics and culture editor at the paper, at their Sunday lunches on Pacific, who spouted to him truthful bromides about process and patience, and, above all – it did not please him to say this - process and patience in lieu of a degree.

Goodman, understanding this to be part of the conversation and procession of hierarchy, would nod, thanks appreciation. All the while the spectral urge lost a millimeter of its diameter every time it was stalled.

On occasion he would send ideas to film and entertainment editors down in Los Angeles, disparate thoughts on the history of the Puyallap and the Nez Perce and the Coeur d'Alene to the Seattle Times. He even sent a couple of ideas about the pending situation on the Korean peninsula to a small newspaper in Hawaii he soon learned had been shuttered, and then later on a slew of unreality to various pulp and trade and more literary imprints from Monterrey to Santa Rosa. He continued to spend his days tracking down stories, sports scores, crime summaries, human interest (mostly of old San Francisco), wheeling them back to the office where he would give them legs, arms and bodies only to have them fade into nothingness, or occasionally verified and glossed realities, but rarely, if ever, under his name. When the day completed, he would drive back to his apartment on Page Street, where he would again expend the best and most dynamic of his energies which he stuffed into envelopes and parted from at a small corner mailbox the following morning before getting back into his car.

One morning Goodman spotted a man walking southward, from the direction of the Panhandle toward Buena Vista Park. He walked, but he didn't just walk. He *moved* (walking is merely within the penumbra of moving: directional moving, moving of limited dimension), up, down, peripherally, around. His black jeans were fitted perfectly, unlike Goodman's, and his boots had fine thick colored laces and his body was muscled and toned and his beard, though blunt of any facial context, was evenly trimmed. But he had no shirt, and Tim - who, in abidance of San Francisco summer, wore closed shoes, jeans, sweater, hat - had no mode for narrating this. But the man kept moving south, toward him, one step followed by a different kind of step as his central torso stretched and rolled, muscle lending way to bone, ab to rib. His closed eyes suggested to Tim that he enjoyed this bodily fluidity greatly, his bare skin greeted by weather that Tim, constitutionally synonymous as far as wind and glare and temperature, once knew as autumn.

Apart from my other justifications for caring about her – she was smart, funny, clever, calm, soulful, generous, ambitious, text-quick – was that she was the first person I really told about my accident. Nor did she ever avert her gaze. She sat and stood there with material answers, with wonderances where answers didn't exist or suffice, with a patting hand that felt like healthy embrace, like warmth. I'm not sure how. She seemed to me like the type of person who hadn't come particularly close to tragedy in her upbringing.

Maybe it had to do with just that; that those who haven't felt the fire can sometimes think about it pretty clearly. It took time; we first discussed it in a computer lab, I applying for jobs and her internships, on a Friday night, and I told her – this was weeks after she first approached me on the staircase – describing it, misleadingly, as *merely* something scary and unfortunate and disruptive that had happened to me. I recall imbibing laughter even.

But I eventually told her the truth: that I didn't find it funny at all. That before the computer lab I had never really sought to describe it. That I was still learning how.

With my parents, who picked me up from the wreckage on a service road just off the highway and under the ventilation of an Elizabeth refinery, I didn't really have to explain, the roof of their Honda Accord shattered just yards away as I nested, hands down and silent, in the pool of my mom's arms. And for a while after I chose not to.

But articles later – articles that had nothing to do with the accident directly, but, being musings about the serious and varying state of the world, derived from its pool of solemnity - I became eager for a person to tell. Not a person to drink with, not a person with whom to talk about classism, careerism or global inequity with, but a person to tell.

I narrated what happened on the highway, though the swerve, brake, flip and crash of my recollection continued to not front with the contours, according to Google Maps, of the road. I described the strangeness of the aftermath, of coming across the George Washington Bridge in a perfectly balanced car thinking that we would sail off the steel and into the width of the Hudson. I patterned far-removed colors of emotion that I had lost to space in the near year since it happened.

All the while Sarah remained there, weaving a note of casual surprise whenever I began to lift my head from the grass, telling me to shove it at my insistence that I was taking up her time and that we should stop discussing the matter entirely ("perchance a sign of my need for a therapist"), parlaying my woes into a broader, eloquent – but believable - canvas. And when I would finally stand up for good - rallying and carrying my disembarked self to my room or the library to finish the work minimally required for my graduating, for my going back to New York - Sarah, with almost no effort, no pretension, no war between progenitor thought and refracted counterpart, with strength I could only visualize, theorize, headed back to the lab, continuing through the delta of streaming occurrent life.

August 2009

To Bill Keller:

*Look around you - oh wait! I forgot you couldn't see through
your Calder! But let's do an exercise: look, again, around you, the
twenty feet to your ceiling, the fifty feet to your far-side living room
window, through the walls to your sitting and standing rooms
and kitchen and bedrooms. Then look, after that, to the tip of
Manhattan Island, to the close-by east and west, up to Riverdale,
down to The Battery. Then, after that, look even further, west into
the heartland, north into Canada, south and east into the ocean.
It gets darker, doesn't it? Then, look into and past the quiet, up
into the cold, past the ocean, to where our continent ends but the
other one, the eastward one, begins. Cross it whole, I dare you.
Scope its beauty, sure – often it is beautiful – but really: look at it.
Look at that which still stands and that which doesn't, that which
has been re-created thousands of times, by war, by demand, by
decree, by urge of fashion. Look past all the "have you been there
I heard it's amazing" toward the places whose ratios begin to lean
toward destroyed and less toward maintained. The flux places. The
tampered places. The places of pain: the pain of losing what's yours
– and, in the process, yourself – over and over again. Remember
that pain: it is deadly valuable, like a French door, like a Klimt or
Schiele. Grab a rock disembarked from a former concrete whole, get
on a plane, cab to your apartment and place that rock in the most*

118

spacious and minimalist of rooms you have. Don't be shy about keeping it in something transparent, a water pitcher, a porron, a santino. Learn to cherish the bottle-bound substance. Put some next to your computer, enough in view so that the eye cannot dictate word without perceiving substance.

Death toll from the war: 655,000.

Upon dinner's completion I found myself in my room again – it had been a notably quiet evening – trying to put a song on before bed. But the Spotify app was kinking and buffering. On the screen's top left the words *Song to Woody* sat in thin Gotham in the search bar, with no recall below. I pressed the home button and flicked the screen upward to "X" out the application before reopening the black and green icon, which welcomed me to the app's front page, already saved to memory. I tried again in the search bar: no successful buffer. I tried again. Then again.

A failed student. An ex-journalist. Later, when back east, he worked as an editor, a replicator of old books nearing the brink of un-circulation. He worked as a disc jockey for a jazz station. He substituted his income with local freelancing and, later, when the local papers and the neighborhood and suburban imprints around Boston began drying up, taught as a substitute. In the summer he sailed people around Buzzards Bay in a Sunfish, to New Bedford, to South Dartmouth, to Cuttyhunk, to the elbow of Cape Cod. When he went back to Taos he helped build houses, helped plan and organize the municipality's measly policy budget free of charge. He befriended all the artists in the area – R.C. Gorman, Judy Chicago, Larry Bell. One time, and for a flat rate, he went down to Marfa to help Donald Judd truck a fleet of squared chairs and dream-colored panels, turquoise and candescent hot pink, to a showing in Detroit, and when he got there spent most of his time in one room, where he unloaded then envisioned then arranged the inputs and, once the show opened, spent forty-eight hours deciding what to do and where to go next.

In the mid-nineties, having become a New York City school-teacher years before, he drove up to New Haven one weekend to talk to the undergraduate dean at Yale, a Santa Fe native with whom he happily discussed Thompson Peak, Bandelier, the Taos art community. Goodman then offered his story: that the school had never formally kicked him out – very politely, he informed them in writing that he would be taking a leave of absence– to which the dean handed *him* his letter, found in the class of '64's files, and, quite amiably, without seeking additional consultation, said he was welcome to come back to Yale to complete his final three years of work.

Heading home, Goodman was pleased but not as pleased as he had expected. He wondered why he had returned. And then: nothing. Nothing came to mind – just the truck and car of the interstate. It was around the Fourth of July, and his younger sister Ella, whom he generally saw just about twice a year, once in the winter and once down in Buzzards Bay, was coming into town. For what reason Tim wasn't entirely certain, but he was sure it wasn't just to solely see him. He would be eating with her at a place near him (but not too near him) that he had recommended. He chose to think about none of it. And in the wake of their encounter, he forgot – not forgot, neglected – to write to his dean to request formal reinstatement, first for a weekend, then for a week, and then... It was January and there he was in a room full of primary Spanish speakers, teaching them a history of dire curricular and holistic limitation, to Albany's requirements. He gathered that that's where he'd stay. He never sent the letter – never thought about sending it.

Summer, 1964

South down pavement, through the green and blue and knotted
white. How you anticipate the water. From nearly every elevated
vantage in San Francisco you can see water, but it's not this *water.*
And here it comes. Padanaram Village passes, a prelude to the
Opening, *and then it happens: your first sighting of Bay, the harbor*
a yard of waywardly parked sailboats. You look out to as far as
you can see - given the turn of the land, this is limited. You keep
driving down pavement. Your mind becomes a tool of the past, of
meanings present and undisclosed: the glass-framed nautical map of
Buzzards Bay, a monoculture of fragile knitwear and timid cotton
padding, the kitchen, the bedrooms, the porch from which you can
see the north bay, up to New Bedford, up to Fairhaven, where the
original house was. You think about all the money, pre-petroleum
and post, that carried itself from the Hudson Valley to Natal to San
Francisco to Macau and back to that house, back to Chicago, back
to Cold Spring. Images come to your head, strange and demonic:
smokestacks, casinos, trains, dead animals, hurt hearts, colonized
heads, smokestacks again.

They are not enough to sour the image of the bay when you
see it again, out of your car, on your porch, when you look out
northward toward Fairhaven. This time you see a quilt of a different,
more integrated kind: of flesh, the scared and the sick, shooting out

123

past Cuttyhunk's curved uninhabited terra into the ocean. You see families parted. You see naked want, malice. You see aspirational love. You see the quests, violent and loving, destructive and creative, desirous and biding, that became us.

"And so to me, it's pretty clear what to do," said Vera. Our conversation had long veered away from the reading. I silently waited for her response.

"Reify the global Comintern?" I said, which Vera and Tony found quite funny and everyone else marginally so.

"It has something to do," she went on, "with the idea of turning everything that is not the heart or mind into a function."

I let her continue.

"That everything – and money is the marquis example of this – is a tool for bolstering those horizons."

"Right," I said. "The market too."

"The government," she added.

It was a conversation that had begun with the efficacy of international institutions and what they ought to be able to do – the answer: more than they do now – which is where everyone else in the class appeared to still be located. The questions were too big – and, frankly, too appealing - for young people who would be forced into the corners of administrative upkeep and systems mastery and code progeneration. But the seminar leader, his Grensons still raised, let us proceed on with our plentiful thoughts. The seminars existed for us to talk. We were paying to go here to talk.

III

I facetimed Sarah about twenty hours after it happened, in the wake of a whole sixteen hours of repeated contact with Ella, with Mom and Dad, with six different employees of Berkshire Medical Center – one internal physician, two specialists, one nurse practitioner, one nurse, one resident – with the Pittsfield police department, with Goodman's personal physician, and, slow-approaching but painful, with the slow barrage of inquiries, both by email and landline, of what happened to him, surging into the later hours of the evening when I had retired to my room, at which point Sarah called.

It was midnight. I was in bed, recently asleep but fully so. Then, just after 1, a perceptible thump, but to my interpretation the kind of thump you hear during the slow adjusting of furniture, rid of emotion or meaning save for the raw facts of weight and contact. A hard step on the way to the bathroom. At most, a restless inspiration to recreate his room before he had to wake up and live with it again in the morning. I sunk back into bed to the distant sounds of the house, the light swirling of the fan, the soft revolutions of my breath.

Then: sounds more rambling. Shuffling and spaced, like the original sound was trying to rediscover its body. No trace of human accompaniment, no groan, no gasp, no plea. This kept me bedbound for another sixty seconds before I heard the sound of Ella's voice from our lone occasion for discussion. I weighed my obligation to check on his trip to the bathroom, or his restless self-license to pace or rearrange, and seconds later I was in the dark of his room trying to locate him before I heard, now in my aural radar, whispered heaves, pained but expectant. Not of someone trying to revert but of someone willing on the point of inflection. The desire for the world to part toward the necessary place of destination. The completion of an episode fully circumambulated. He called for no one.

I grabbed the laptop from under my bed - I had not used it once the entire month - ran down one staircase, then the second, the computer softly in the firmness of my wrist but not my arm, like a cocky running back. I sat myself in the small alcove to the right of the basement staircase, in the sight of the workshop. I turned on the computer, input the Wi-Fi. I typed "Google Maps" into the search bar and clicked on a blue button with a black arrow and typed in directions, first A, then B. I typed in Berkshire Hospital to slot B, accidentally typing "Bersire". Autocorrect. Buffering.

I placed Goodman in the backseat, his head one door and feet the other, and angled the laptop toward me in the front seat. It said it would take thirty-three minutes.

The entire ride he did me the favor of what a lifetime of conspicuous male movement gave to him so easily: overt physical deliberation. He syncopated his breaths incongruously so that for every whisper there was a groan. He pounded his heels on the seating's vinyl. He dragged his arms on the backrest, visible tokens of pain, possible preludes to a body muted and drowned but ones that for now implied a gruesome totality, continuity.

I rushed the car around the hospital pull-up circle, halted, and began trying to get him from the seat to the lobby. I felt, for the first time – and contrary to getting him into the car, for which he gave me interstitial help: foot shuffling, hip flexing, calf and thigh condensing – the full weight of Goodman's body. His eyes were still open, but the type of open that didn't seem open. *This is a moment* did not appear to be going through his head. Even in a world where smiles can be sorrow and frowns joy, his face, to me, and similar to the breaths I heard in the bedroom, looked determinative: either he knew this wasn't a moment of pivot, that we would be back on Vandermeer by morning – somnambulantly we would come and somnambulantly we would go – or that it *was* a moment of pivot but what was there to do? The clock had already been set (and no one gets to decide the length of minutes and seconds).

"What happened?" The sight of a resident through the revolving doors, her eyes parting from phone.
  "Fell off the bed in his sleep.'"
  "No, I mean, *what happened?*"
  "Right. I'm really not sure. Stroke maybe?"
  "You didn't ask?"
  "He's nonverbal."
  "Conscious?"
  "Definitely conscious."
  "Has he been having problems?"
  "Yes" – I didn't want to get too into it – "but none that he's really told me about."
  "Does he have someone he sees?"
  "Yes, someone across the border. I can't remember his name."
  She sailed down the hallway. All was silent except for the building – twenty-first century silence: light circuits, pipes (metal and water), furnaces, cooling systems, medical equipment, card-friendly vending machines, a pay-by-hour charging station

for your phone, a TV that played a muted red-chyroned CNN, another muted TV playing local news.

Four footsteps tapping the linoleum followed by a necessary exchange of information, the information I told the resident but which I now told to the attending, followed by an examination of the body, Tim still technically there, the peak of his stomach in fast, reverting palpitation, followed by inquiries about the occurrences of recent hours, followed by inquiries about medical history.

The questions were followed by professional endearances (not too specific, not too general, not too fake, not too vital), followed by the deployment of two additional staff of uncertain title to help lift Tim up into a wheelchair, with which I helped, as he was rolled into the back of the hospital.

He died bed-bound just as the sun was coming up around five. It didn't take long to figure out what had happened: for months, his heart's left ventricle had been working irregularly, meagerly – this he knew from his doctor, but had decided not to tell anyone; certainly not me but nor, I learned later, his sister – which had impacted his heart's circulation and, subsequently, his stiffened, bloodless lower body, which carried on with ample but wavering circulation. But when night finally came, and the left ventricle stopped fulfilling its minimal operational denominator, the heart's fluidal balance, like a boat in drowning capsize, tipped from the ventricle through the lungs and into the heart's right chambers - which, like vessels starved of length and width, failed - and then into the rest of the body, the blood in crowded recession as it came to a passive and extended halt.

That evening, for the first time since I had driven up to New Lebanon, I spoke with Ella. I had spent a full sleepless day as Tim's logistician – questions as to how he wished to process his body (he had made it very clear to me, on a spare trip to the supermarket, that he wished ultimately to be cremated, a topic upon which, pertaining to my own body and my wholly un-immediate circumstances, I concurred), calls to family and friends, conversations regarding a timeline for formal recognition. I would confirm with Ella, though I was pretty confident I had an idea for that too: the Unis in Pittsfield, where Tim would occasionally pay respect in between errands and car rides and intermittent exchanges on God and whether She or He should be respected out of the fact of their existence, or whether they *could* exist, or if, even if they didn't exist, it is a mightily aspirational and additive and healthy game to want them to. I knew the exact building too, brick with a white door, though I had never gone inside.

Polite and kindly deferent, Ella said she had been considering the Unis or the Old Chatham Quakers, where Tim had also turned suppositions of curiosity into stints of attendance. She said she would call the Unis immediately to make arrangements, adding that she was "phenomenally sorry" she couldn't be there for the prior, and momentous, twenty-four hours, and that she would be to New Lebanon by Saturday.

Of course, she told me, I was free to go home. I told her that I'd be happy to stay and together we found ourselves trapped in a fog of limited articulative energy and politeness, ending the call with no definitive plan. So I stayed, with no desire as of yet to go home and with two cars in the driveway, with books on the shelf, with select VHS' of Truffaut and *The Phil Silvers Show* in a TV room next to Tim's bedroom.

One night after getting takeout I sat in the living room with a long pamphlety hardback when my eyesight shifted from to the top of the next page to the stick figures near the front door. I first thought about Goodman painting them - whether it was in retirement or on a weekend up from the city. And then: *Small streams of individuality, phenotype…The direction in which we choose to dance…* before faring back to the page.

The day before the funeral Mom and Dad drove up from Westchester. We drove to Great Barrington, discussing fabric, Ravel (as we passed Tanglewood) and Trump on our way through the vivacious Berkshire summer and, when we got there, moved into and out of clothing and record and boutique good stores. Before long we were elbows on table at a Thai restaurant in silence, Mom and Dad seated vertically, their phones and eyes separated only by glasses - Mom's rectangular, Dad's circular - as they angled their gazes down, Mom utilizing her pointer finger, Dad his thumbs. A suggestion that Mom was surfing and Dad was texting or emailing.

The next morning we gathered in the old Georgian mansion that had been converted, devotional glass circling the pews, the pews circling a ten-bulb chandelier. The light was browned by the stains of the many devotionals, the colors decisive and representative: the green and red of linen, the brown of earth, the royal blue of ambient sky.

Some comers were suited but most were cuffed with cotton, belted and shoe-clad in leather, clothed between waist and foot in khaki. They sat, slow-jointed and erect, as the priest stood at the nave in a singular cassock, his collar white, beard gray, his soft tenor suggestive of the working metropolis to the church's east rather than its south, his speech conversant and au fait. The type of guy you'd trust for a book recommendation or a Celtics playoff reminiscence. I hadn't a clue what his connection was to Goodman, but he spoke of him in the familiar, and when he finished he invited Ella up to the nave who, though polite and accommodating and tentative in one on one, transformed into author and narrator, willing sections of laughter and nodding and deep listening as she weaved through stories of disillusionment and discovery, overreach and asceticism, pain and joy, loneliness and the flooding onset and re-retrieval of community: Civil Rights in college, Free Speech in San Francisco, anti-war communitarianism and drugs in New Mexico (faint laughs), spearheading Mom's reading project at Cedar Junction in the late 70s, his first job teaching in Dorchester, the Institute - an art and artisanal collective he founded when he moved back to New Mexico that eventually ran out of money for its admirable end (to unite indigent art with the high art of Californian and Texan ranch parties, to untie artistic quality from price and access) - his next and last teaching job in Harlem, the places to which he had been in the interregnum of time and calling: to India in the 70s (where he'd met a near-partner, an Aussie), to Paris and Belgium with Dad to see the village in Wallonia where he'd been cooped up during the War.

I sat back, knuckles pressed together, slouched but especially eager and bought-in, combining and arranging the strokes of a man I knew for only a concentrated period of time. That I barely did know.

There were conceptions that we carried with us through time. At some moments they felt like the weight of a car and at others, pixie dust. This was because our minds played with us. Or no, they didn't play with us. They just struggled with what minds often do: reaching beyond the prism of perception to a place of omniscience.

And so we never knew if we were shepherds or dogmatists (the worst kind, the type that treat dubious perception as the gold of civilization), penitents or charlatans, originalists or salesmen. But I – with my very common degree of understanding of what was real and what was not real, what I meant and didn't mean – went forward, sober but not acolytic, against the idea that liberty and ideal had given way to cultural degeneration, that selfishness of time and journey had given way to selfishness of money and property. These of course were the primary criticisms of that time. But maybe it was this: that the future we clamored for with nascent shape and limited direction would come at a riper, more ready time. That it would lose by 48 and 49 odd states but that eventually it would come, decades and quarter and half and full centuries later. That the green of the country's grass would be especially green, especially watered, as it sat under the cool evening of an early November night as the national machinery fell into place, a sieve of breathing flowing opinion filtered down to a basic affirmation or negation on soul and identity. The noise of the predictive complex – polling, demographic arithmetic, qualitative consultancy – would stall, and it would be so especially silent, static as art, stern as nature, blank but for the glare of window-proximate TVs that hoisted athletes and stars and anchors...

Down Fleet Street, past the columned pantheon of St. Paul's face, down the steps and between the cables, feet unmoving on the perforated steel. I turn left, splay my forearms on the railing elbow to wrist as I look out on the eastern city, from where the boats came from Denmark and Gaul. But the intimacy of that story can only be rendered street by street. Here, the city is as much as its vertical orientation, the Shard on the south bank and Liverpool Street's futuristic cluster to its north. To my fore (going counterclockwise), Mayfair and the peak of that indubitable Ferris Wheel around the river bend, the willing confluence – whether healthily shaped or indented and abbreviated, whether of meaning wholesome or frilled – of old and new.

I thought about the perch in Hastings, the one on the property of the public library, forged first in fire then carved in ice, by the glacier that deposited at run's end Manhattan and Long Island and created the vista on which I was standing, and from which, the cliffs spanning an immaculate southwest diagonal down to the island's northernmost point, New Rome was created, replacing the one I stood within. From where the century's most extraordinary and impactful and difficult events took place: the plane that followed the river's path - that sang over the library's head - toward the southern end of the city; the banks which rendered the world's economy a cavern as the buildings which held them quietly and emptily stood in place; the hatted party thrown in a black tower with block yellow letters; the virus that pressed and weaned onto glass, metal and air. All of it compressed into proximity for the sake of a soul over water, one looking outward and across at commerce and human relations at its most developed and pocketed and manic, at creation physical and virtual, at water.

I reach the big metal doors that look like half-resting eyes and wait with the other riders. When the doors finally open we enter into a prismatic space and wait as the floor sinks beneath us. Twenty seconds later we come to a stop as we exit onto the tube platform, the walls edging outward then inward as they rise toward the ceiling, the same oval as the cars that ease into and out of the stations. Two minutes later my headphones are plugged and tightened as we edge toward the Thames' subterrain. My phone plan keeps me from accessing anything other than music already saved and queued, the same material I tread over day after day on my walk to school. Though I find something fresh. Something to which I hadn't listened since Tim had bid me find it the previous summer.

"Oh, my loving mother, when the world's on fire," Lesley Riddle wrote.
"My little darling, oh, how I love you," Maybelle Carter wrote.
"This land is your land," Woody Guthrie wrote.
Goodman transitioned through the songs, their first minute at a time as the man who inspired the exercise sat on the computer screen downstairs, kind eyes, thin goatee. He clarified that the object wasn't enjoyment. And when he got through all three he said nothing, but instead got up, found his cane and walked toward the kitchen.

Following his death this never translated into any summation, but it did, ironically, pour into other sonic revelations. The panorama of noise, from the puddy sound of the household to the scratch of drugged transmogrification to death, in the Velvet Underground. The sound of the Native hymn, of the expanse of the great plain, in Terry Riley, Neil Young, Sufjan Stevens.

These also led to revelations more general about thieving, sharing, maintaining, coexisting; sounds and stories that became more powerful upon my daily aging, but often more powerful – as it did with Riddle, Carter and Guthrie - became less hashed. That the revelations continued in a difficult, commingled residence that was at once determined to remember and love, change and stay, disavow and be. That the heritage, the gift, still outlasted the opacity and pain and impossibility of the mystery.

Shera,

I just went to the doctor. I am fine but I am also not doing too great. I am sorry if that doesn't make sense but really it is my best way of expressing my current state. But the reason I'm writing to you is – as it always is - because of a reminiscence. I am sorry about all these late-night reminiscences - ones that I write to you at 3am, hours before my normally timed correspondences. I guess it keeps me going even as my body refuses to sit and rest within.

    It is about the time you solicited my help moving from White Plains to Mahopac. But the memory has nothing to do with the packing or driving of that small truck over the county line. It had to do with when we got to the house, a ranch-like first floor – the top floor - over a garage dug into the area's gradient. I don't know why it was so beautiful. There you were, with your jeans and sneakers and tucked-in plaid shirt, with a chaise lounge and a just-procured king-sized bed and Priya's accounting cabinets in the truck, looking out at the house and back at me, your wife and daughter still on their way in the CR-V. It stood there while you looked at it, like you were unsure if it would stay. The lawn was anything but kept – blotches of brown, shades of yellow and green – and immediately I pictured you there in mere years, when Tejal was a high schooler, out on that lawn and waving at passersby. You would have two cars, one parked in the garage and one in the concrete lot between the street and garage which blocked a basketball rim at the bottom of the driveway that resembled nothing close to standard play and which would go unused, your daughter having found a new source of meaning to and from which you would drive her (and, one day, to which she would drive herself), from which you would pick her up after you got home from work, her in a slight slouch and, at least in the mid-teen years, before it all became brutally common, where you'd be waiting for her, fully out of the car, hands concealed in cloth, chest back, legs erect, hips forward as you and the big gray car look out at her and smile. And all of it will feel as if you've never done anything else. And you, like her, will be a little bored. That boredom. Bored at home. Peering. Waiting.

London *2015*
New York City *2022*

Acknowledgements

I would like to acknowledge the many people that dedicated time – whether minutes, hours, days – to helping me conceive of how a novel of such thematic, narrative and vocal variation could work; how it could be interesting while true. My partner Abby; my sister-in-law Anneli; my cousin Sara Houghteling; my aunt Elizabeth Fishel; friends, including Marco Martellini, Kevin Sweeting, Hannah Goldberg-Morse and others. To all the people who inhabit my many past places: Hastings, Hackley, Claremont, London, New York. To Sam, my standard for what it means to be mindful, serious, hilarious, giving. And, lastly, to Mom, a singular force for creativity and morality in my life, who taught me that if you can find that special mix of strength and sight to remember, forgive, connect (even with that which seems most distant or irreconcilable), then have no fear, you will sleep.

About the Author

Jack Houghteling grew up in Hastings on Hudson, NY and holds degrees from Claremont McKenna College and the London School of Economics. His debut novel GOODMAN was longlisted for the Dzanc Books Prize for Fiction.

Made in the USA
Las Vegas, NV
17 October 2022

57507108R00085